Orthopaedic Injuries
of the
Cibil War

An Atlas of Orthopaedic Injuries

and Treatments During the Civil War

by Julian E. Kuz, M.D., and Bradley P. Bengtson, M.D.

Kennesaw Mountain PRESS

in association with

M.S.

Medical Staff Press, L.L.C.

Published by
Kennesaw Mountain Press, Inc., Kennesaw, Georgia
1810 Old Highway 41, Kennesaw, Georgia 30152
Telephone (770) 424-5225

in association with

Medical Staff Press, L.L.C.
4286 Knapp Valley Court
Grand Rapids, Michigan 49505
Telephone (616) 363-8655
E-mail: CIVILMED@aol.com
http://www.bluemarble.net/~civilmed

The authors invite comments, corrections, and additional information from the readers. New information is most appreciated and will be acknowledged in future editions of this book. Correspondence can be addressed to the authors in care of Medical Staff Press at the address above.

Additional copies of this title can be ordered for $9.95 plus $3.00 shipping and handling from Medical Staff Press at the address above.

LIBRARY OF CONGRESS CATALOGING IN PUBLICATION DATA

Kuz, Julian E., and Bengtson, Bradley P.
ORTHOPAEDIC INJURIES OF THE CIVIL WAR
#96-75433

ISBN 0-9635861-7-3

Typography and design by Nancy Dearing Rossbacher
Fit To Print Desktop Publishing Services
Post Office Drawer 631, Orange, Virginia 22960

Dedication

This book is dedicated to our wives and families
for their constant support and
welcome of new adventures:

Cheryl Kuz, M.D.
&
Tami, Brittney, and Brielle Bengtson

ON THE COVER:

Surgeon General's Office
Army Medical Museum

Photographs No's. 132, 133. *Amputation of both thighs for gunshot injury.*

Private Columbus G. Rush, Company C, 21st Georgia Regiment. Was wounded March 25, 1865, in an assault on Fort Steadman in the lines before Petersburg, Virginia, by a fragment of shell which laid open the right knee joint and shattered the upper third of the left tibia and produced great laceration of the soft parts of the left leg. He was made a prisoner, and four hours after the reception of the injury he was placed under chloroform and both thighs were amputated by the antero-posterior flap method at the lower thirds by surgeon D.W. Bliss, U.S.F. The patient was removed to the Base Hospital at City Point and thence, on March 17, 1865, to Lincoln Hospital at Washington. In August 1865, he was sent to St. Luke's Hospital in New York, and on February 22, 1866, he was furnished with subscription with artificial limbs, adapted by Dr. E.D. Hudson. With the aid of two canes he was able to walk about the wards of St. Luke's. His residence is at Atlanta, Georgia. His appearance while at Lincoln Hospital is shown in photographs of surgical cases, S.G.O. Volume 3, No. 36.

Photographed at the Army Medical Museum.

By order of the Surgeon General:

GEORGE A. OTIS
Bv't. Lt. Col., Ass't Surgeon, U.S.A., Curator, A.M.M.

Acknowledgments

The authors would like to thank the following individuals and organizations,
without whose help and support this book would not have been possible:

Lawrence E. Pawl
and Jack W. Melton, Jr.,
Kennesaw Mountain Press

Michael Rhode,
Curator, Otis Archives
National Museum of Health and Medicine

Troy Pierce, M.D.

Martin Kuz

Alfred B. Swanson, M.D.

Joanie Hodson,
Plastic Surgery Associates,
Grand Rapids, Michigan

Susan Gell-Meyers
Janet Knause,
and Jay Smith,
Warner Norcross and Judd

Susan Rankin,
Old Kent Bank

Ronald Vanderlaan, M.D.,
Blodgett Memorial Medical Center
and Blodgett Medical Journal

George Rable,
Department of History,
Anderson University

National Museum of Civil War Medicine
Frederick, Maryland

Trade Typographers

Gustavo Colon, M.D.

Gamma Photo,
Chicago, Illinois

Nancy Dearing Rossbacher,
North South Trader's CIVIL WAR magazine
and
Fit To Print Desktop Publishing Services

Grand Rapids Orthopaedic Surgery
Residency Program

Our friends and family

Table of Contents

I.

Preface

The American Civil War has had a significant impact on many areas of medicine in the United States. The need for a large-scale, dedicated medical corps and the great number of casualties stimulated changes in all aspects of surgical practices. One of the areas most influenced by the war has been the field of orthopaedic surgery, with the Civil War serving as the impetus for the eventual formation of the specialty in the United States.

While many dramatic discoveries in the area of orthopaedic surgery were not to be uncovered until the twentieth century, many of the basic procedures and techniques were developed during this war and continue to be used today. Examples include various types of traction, splints, wound treatment, and a wide variety of surgical procedures. Over 70% of all injuries during the war involved the extremities, creating a dramatic gain in the knowledge of surgery in this area.

A number of other references have discussed the development of the respective medical corps, surgeon lifestyles, biographies of physicians, and general descriptions of surgery done during the period. Presented in this work is an anatomical approach to the soldier injuries and surgical interventions performed by Civil War surgeons. We will also discuss complications and mortality rates for specific injuries and methods of treatment. The diversity of treatments comes during an era where scientific study was just becoming the basis for determining which procedures would provide the most favorable outcome. Also included are cases with photographs by anatomical region to provide a more specific account of treatments and outcomes.

II.
Introduction

Civil War medicine is a topic not widely covered in historical discussions of that era. A number of books available on the subject discuss the development of the respective medical corps, surgeon lifestyles, biographies of physicians, and general descriptions of surgery done during the period. Up to this point, a detailed discussion of extremity trauma surgery during the war has not been available. The authors of this reference have attempted to compile an atlas of specific surgical options and treatments that Civil War surgeons employed to treat a variety of wounds. The diversity of treatments seen comes during an era in which scientific study was just becoming the basis for determining which procedures would provide the most favorable outcomes. We need to recall how the often squalid conditions, the fact that the medical corps had to follow mobile armies, the lack of good lighting, inadequate instrumentation, empirical studies, and the absence of many of the tenets of modern medicine have ultimately influenced Civil War orthopaedic surgery.

The text of this book is separated by anatomic region. This is essentially the way that orthopaedic trauma management is presented in most of today's textbooks on the subject. The surgeons of the time often had average educations, little training early in the war, and a paucity of clinical experience. This fact, combined with the enormous number of casualties, led to a lack of standardization of treatments. Many of the anatomic sections on treatment represent this variety.

In addition to the text, representative photographs have been included based on the anatomic location of injuries. These photographs represent one of the first significant contributions to medical photography made here in the United States and are from *Photographs of Surgical Cases and Specimens.* They document the types of injuries and surgical outcomes that occurred during the American Civil War, as well as a number of miscellaneous civilian and Indian War injuries. They serve as visual studies at a time when physicians were struggling to classify these injuries and standardize treat-

This work marks the first detailed study of extremity trauma surgery during the tumultous War Between the States.

While the medical value of the case studies in the Otis Archives has diminished, the historical value has increased.

ments for the sometimes horrifying injuries caused by the weapons of this period. The photographs were collected, during a period from 1866 to 1872, by the Surgeon General's Office in order to meet those educational needs. George A. Otis, M.D., was the compiler of this large work. This collection, along with *The Medical and Surgical History of the War of the Rebellion*, remain the most important set of archival material regarding the medical history of the war. While *The Medical and Surgical History* has been reprinted, the photographs and case reports of the Otis Archives have not been widely available in over 100 years.

The lack of a reissue of these photos may be due to their perceived medical value in the past, along with high publication and distribution costs. As the weapons of war changed rapidly and the medical/surgical treatments advanced, the photos became more irrelevant to the medical establishment on a clinical basis. This is the same process that occurs even today to all medical textbooks. However, while their medical value has diminished, their historical value has become ever greater. The twenty.case reports included in this book are but a smattering of the monumental collection of eight such volumes totaling 400 photographs and case reports compiled by Otis. A reprint of these volumes and an additional 150 assorted photographs will be available in the spring of 1996 from these publishers.

When looking at these pictures, one can begin to learn of the nature of injury and treatment during this period. The soldiers had volunteered to be photographed and thus contribute to the medical knowledge of the time. These photos not only assisted the men in their pension requests but assisted future physicians in dealing with these kinds of disfigurement and injury. It is also the most graphic depiction of the severe sacrifices these men on both sides made for a cause in which they firmly believed.

This publication serves to display one more aspect of the most important historical period in our nation's history. It is an aspect that has not always received equal attention as that given to the battles and generals. Nevertheless, this period played an important role in shaping medicine and surgery in the United States and, more specifically, the specialty of orthopaedics.

III.

Background

The American Civil War was a watershed event that forever changed our political, military, social, and medical thinking. Orthopaedic surgery, at the time of the war, was not as yet a recognized specialty in the United States. The roots of American orthopaedic surgery take their impetus from this event. Today's view of surgery during this conflict is often similar to how a Confederate physician may have felt when he noted "[fellow surgeons] condemning compound fractures of the extremities to the knife with as little hesitancy as if men's limbs, like those of the salamander, were reproduced with great certainty."[1] The orthopaedic treatments of the time were considerably richer in variety and thoughtfulness than represented by this common misconception.

The Civil War (1861-65) occurred during a period of American medicine that some authors refer to as the "middle ages." Joseph Lister did not publish his famous papers on antisepsis until 1867—two years after the war was over. It would be a number of years before American physicians would accept and apply his antiseptic principles. The concept that bacteria as a source for infection was being formulated in Europe but would not arrive before war's end. Although it had been known since 1843 that puerperal sepsis could be spread by hand contamination, this teaching was ignored. The treatment of shock with blood products and intravenous fluid resuscitation remained unknown, although there were two recorded attempts of blood transfusion for hemorrhage during the war, with one successful outcome.[2]

During the Civil War, the stethoscope, thermometer, and hypodermic needle were not employed extensively, although they were available in some areas. The advent of modern orthopaedics would await the invention of the *x*-ray by Roentgen in 1895 and corrosive resistant alloys and antibiotics in the first part of this century.

Despite the obvious disadvantage that the Civil War trauma surgeon had compared to his modern-day counterparts, orthopaedic treatments were formulated, refined, and enhanced. Improvements in hospitals, wound care, the

A.
General Information

use of anesthesia, ambulances, and nursing care also aided in the treatment of injured soldiers. Some examples of advancement in orthopaedic treatment included Buck's traction, use of plaster splints, open treatment of contaminated wounds, and the development of specialty orthopaedic and prosthetic hospitals. Several of the first attempts in the United States to repair fractures with wire (open reduction-internal fixation) occurred during the war. Excision arthroplasties with removal of portions of bones and joints, shell fragment extraction, and various types of amputations were improved and refined because of the large number of casualties.

This tremendous magnitude of casualties would advance the knowledge of orthopaedic injuries with a speed unknown in any previous period. More than 600,000 men, of over three million involved—2% of the entire population of the United States at the time—died in the hostilities.[3] More soldiers died of disease than trauma [see Table 1 below]. More than 400,000 injuries and six million cases of sickness—three major illnesses per soldier—were recorded among Union troops alone.[4] Nearly one-half million soldiers came out of the Civil War permanently disabled.[5] These brave soldiers and their huge number of wounds and disabilities provided the experience for advancing both surgical and medical treatments.

The medical corps of the Union and Confederacy were ill prepared to cope with the staggering amount of casualties. The number of trained physicians, their medical education, and the ambulance and hospital systems proved to be woefully inadequate, particularly at the beginning of the war. Both sides had expected a short resolution of the conflict with limited casualties. The number of trained physicians who enlisted grew as the conflict wore on, but a myriad of deficiencies continued. One example of this occurred immediately after the Battle of Gettysburg, when the bulk of the Union medical staff was sent south in preparation for a battle with General Lee's retreating forces that never materialized. The 20,000 wounded remaining at Gettysburg were tended to by less than one-third of the medical staff available. This presented each remaining surgeon with more than 900 surgical cases. Another example is that of one Union surgeon who performed seventy-five amputations in a single morning following the first Battle of Manassas. Commonly, surgeons of either side treated injured soldiers the enemy left behind in the wake of a retreat. This further increased the caseload of each surgeon present. An interesting benefit was an increase in sharing of knowledge as well as an increased rivalry between the surgeons of the different sides. One Union medical officer who had examined a shoulder excision performed by a Southern surgeon at the Battle of Gettysburg went so far as to express "much surprise that a rebel surgeon could perform a difficult operation so successfully." The Confederate surgeon retorted, "How notoriously consistent with Yankee character is the attempt of a Northern brother to defame the reputation and underrate the skill of the Confederate sur-

Table 1. Causes of Troop Deaths [1,44]

	CONFEDERATE	UNION
Killed and mortally wounded in battle	94,000 (est.)	110,070*
Died of disease	150,000 (est.)	249,458
Total dead	244,000 (est.)	359,528

*Mortality rate from wounds alone was 13.3-14.1%.[45]

geons..."[6] Thus, the treatment of extremity trauma was influenced not only by the need to treat large numbers of casualties, but also by surgical biases developed on both sides.

As the war progressed, medical staffs from both the North and South learned that only experienced hands ought to handle certain procedures. Some doctors were designated as "operators," eliminating inexperienced physicians found earlier in the war who were eager to learn how to "cut and carve." This can be viewed as the beginning of specialization. By the end of the war, more than 3,000 medical officers had served for the Confederacy and approximately 11,700 physicians had served in the field or in hospitals for the Union.[1,4] The Civil War eventually provided a large corps of well-trained surgeons and doctors to handle the disabled after the war.

Secondary to the large patient volume, orthopaedic trauma care was advanced by establishing more uniform treatment standards, education, and dissemination of information. The Union and Confederate armies would go on to develop a dedicated ambulance service and a military hospital system that included mobile and large general hospitals. Other advances included the extensive use of anesthetics, the birth of American nursing care, guidelines detailing the type and timing of specific surgical procedures, and advances in the treatment of open wounds.

Medical staffs on both sides realized the need to keep physicians informed about the latest techniques and results of different surgical procedures. The need for this became apparent after several medical inspectors had noticed great variability in treatment for the same types of wounds by different surgeons. Surgical manuals such as *A Manual of Military Surgery for the Use of Surgeons in the Confederate Army* by Julian John Chisolm were often found "in the pockets of the surgeons." The experience accumulated by British surgeon T. Longmore from the Crimean War was published in his *Treatise on Gunshot Wounds* and was issued in large numbers to Union soldiers. In the South, the publication of medical journals stopped. One Confederate surgeon lamented, after noting a poor application of Smith's anterior splint by medical officers, "Articles, we are aware, have been already written on this subject, both in the *American Journal of Medical Sciences* and in the *Virginia and Maryland Medical Journal,* but few of the profession [Confederate physicians], at present, have access to either of these volumes."[7] The need for a Southern medical journal prompted the creation of the *Confederate States Medical and Surgical Journal,* the only medical journal published in the South. It achieved wide circulation, but only near the end of the war.

B. Transportation

Concerning the problem of transportation of the wounded, the war began without a dedicated ambulance service because of poor preparation and planning. Early in the war, the Confederacy instituted a military corps assigned to removal of the injured on the battlefield. Their efficiency was hampered by a lack of ambulances, and they often depended on the capture of Union ambulances for a portion of their supply. The North, meanwhile, developed an assigned corps only after several painful experiences. Initially, the Union army had no dedicated troops for ambulance service and relied on hired teamsters. At the first major encounter of the war, First Battle of Manassas, many hired teamsters handled the casualties roughly or ran away. One observer noted that he doubted any of the Union casualties that day were evacuated by ambulance. Even with its ambulance service, the South experienced similar problems. After the Battle of Chickamauga, it took ten days to get some of the injured to hospitals.[8] Three days after the Battle of Second Manassas, 3,000 men still lay where they had fallen. The last casualties were finally removed by September 9. Pressure on the government and military by Dr. Henry I. Bowditch, a civilian doctor who felt his son's death was partly due to a delayed evacuation during the Peninsular Campaign in 1862, and United States Medical Director Jonathan Letterman eventually created an ambulance corps that showed much improvement by the Battle of Antietam.[4] Problems still occurred at later battles, but from that point onward dedicated ambulances and corps speeded evacuation, improving the chances that men would be in better condition if surgery was required. Transportation of the wounded was also carried out on both sides by rail and waterway—the first time that these modes of transportation of injured troops were used during wartime.

C. Hospitals

Hospitals improved throughout the war. The initial dressing station was usually a tent, barn, church, or private home, where triage and primary surgery was often performed. Surgeons on both sides learned that their patients fared better when surgery was performed outdoors rather than indoors due to improved lighting and ventilation. Efficiency was gained by building larger hospitals and by creating a ward system, still in use in some settings today, separating patients by injuries or disease. The largest hospital on either side, Chimborazo in Richmond, had 8,000 beds.[2] A growing realization that "bad air" and unclean conditions might increase infection led to clean, well-ventilated hospitals.[4] This bad air concept was, however, overemphasized and direct transmission of bacteria through instruments and dressing materials went unrecognized. In the South, due to the rising number of disabled, the medical authorities in February 1865 decided to establish orthopaedic hospitals "for exclusive treatment of old injuries and deformities from gunshot wounds"—another example of early specialization. By March 1865, the Confederate government extended access to these specialty orthopaedic hospitals to soldiers already discharged.[1]

D. Anesthesia

Although in its infancy, anesthesia, even at the onset of the conflict, was routinely employed—this in opposition to a commonly held misconception today and at the time. Indeed, a soldier undergoing surgery without anesthesia was the exception rather than the rule, and it generally occurred only when supplies were exhausted. Chloroform and ether were first used by U.S. troops during the Mexican-American War in 1847.[9] Chloroform was used at least 75% of the time since it was nonflammable, more easily transported, and more readily attainable than ether, especially in the blockaded South. Ether was also found to worsen shock and lower blood pressure and is now known to be a potent vasodilator. Records collected after the war show that of 8,900 examined cases of anesthesia administration, only forty-three deaths could be attributed directly to the anesthetic. This 0.4% mortality rate was remarkable considering the lack of monitoring equipment and supplemental oxygen. The low death rate was ascribed to the open-drop technique, wherein the anesthetic was applied to a cloth held over the patients nose and mouth and withdrawn after the patient was off to sleep.

More than 80,000 cases of anesthesia were reported, a testament to its widespread use. In addition to anesthesia, opium was used for pain control, not only for injuries but for painful dressing changes. The typical way of administering opium was by pill form or by dusting it on the wounds. It is much less effective in the latter form. Near the end of the war it was also being given by hypodermic injection, a much more effective but less common technique.[4]

Contrary to popular belief, anesthesia was more the rule than the exception during the war. A Union soldier receives anesthesia in this image.

E. Nursing Care

The employment of nursing care for American troops was initiated during the Civil War and gave birth to modern nursing as we know it today. Nurses greatly enhanced the care of the soldiers. One nurse, Dorathea Dix, volunteered in 1861 and became Superintendent of Female Nurses for the entire Union army. She screened appointments and initially only allowed unattractive, "mature women" to become nurses. As the war continued and casualties mounted, the need for nurses grew to the point where she dropped her restrictions. Another nurse, Clara Barton, earned the nickname "Angel of the Battlefield" and eventually founded the American Red Cross. Nuns were often employed as nurses in the western campaigns, which resulted in the involvement of the Catholic Church and the eventual expansion of Catholic hospitals in the United States.[10]

An important adjunct to nursing care were the various relief agencies that sprang up. The United States Sanitary Commission in the North provided relief for the beleaguered medical corps by supplying medicine, bandages, educational pamphlets, and volunteers. Numerous organizations also formed in the South, including the Ladies' Hospital of Montgomery, Ladies' Soldiers Relief Society, and the largest: the Association for the Relief of Maimed Soldiers.

F. Wound Care

The wounds from the war were appalling in both incidence and severity. The high numbers of wounds were attributed to the advancement of destructive weapons with a lag in the advancement of fighting tactics. Officers felt that despite the ability to amass firepower, they still required a massed assault in formation to defeat entrenched positions of the enemy. The minié ball, a relatively new development, increased the severity of injuries tremendously because it could rapidly dissipate energy into the surrounding body tissues. Fired from a rifled musket, these large .58 caliber, soft-lead bullets would deform and tumble on impact, causing large wounds. The minié ball had a high velocity for the period, 950 feet per second, and was deadly at 200-300 yards. A surgeon in the Army of the Tennessee wrote, "The shattering, splintering, and splitting of a long bone by the impact of a minié or Enfield ball were, in many instances, both remarkable and frightful..."[1]   Dr. E.L. Howard of the Army of Northern Virginia commented, "...wounds of bony structures, inflicted by this missile, are characterized by extensive fissuring and comminution, such as was rarely, if ever seen, when the old smoothbore musket was the weapon of the soldier."[11]

The type of surgical treatment and the timing of surgery represented the chief decisions faced by trauma surgeons of the period. Records in the South from earlier in the war showed that nearly 65% of all wounds were extremity wounds;[12] twelve separate Union records showed more than 71% of all wounds were of the extremities.[2] Orthopaedic treatment was generally classified into three types: conservative (expectant), excision (resection), or amputation. The philosophy of choosing one of these treatments shifted during the war. As the war continued and surgeons became more experienced, they also became more conservative. There were proponents of resections who felt that life and limb were to be saved by such a surgery. Arguments against resection and for amputation included useless limbs, longer hospital stays, and an increased infection rate.[1] Amputation was regarded as the most aggressive surgical approach. Many surgeons gained the reputation of Saw-bones if their colleagues felt they were quick to amputate a limb. In order to assist surgeons making the decision of whether to amputate or excise, guidelines were distributed in the form of handbooks or in medical journals.[13] These guidelines included amputation if the limb was nearly

Table 2. Results of Various Amputations Performed by Confederate Surgeons [1]

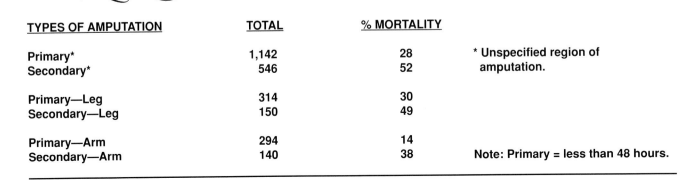

TYPES OF AMPUTATION	TOTAL	% MORTALITY	
Primary*	1,142	28	* Unspecified region of
Secondary*	546	52	amputation.
Primary—Leg	314	30	
Secondary—Leg	150	49	
Primary—Arm	294	14	
Secondary—Arm	140	38	Note: Primary = less than 48 hours.

amputated from the initial injury or if there was extensive soft tissue damage, neurovascular injury of major nerves or blood vessels, or open fractures of the joints or thigh. Recommendations for excision only without amputation included gunshot wounds of the fingers, toes, wrist, shoulder, elbow, and ankle if the major nerves and arteries escaped injury. Resection was only advised if the guidelines for amputation were not met. Also, amputation from gunshot wounds of the upper two-thirds of the thigh and hip joint had such high mortality, surgeons were told not to amputate at these levels. In these areas death from the amputation approached 100%. Amputation was also excluded in cases where the soldier was mortally wounded elsewhere, such as the chest, head or abdomen.[14] The surgical approach also varied based on whether an upper or lower extremity was injured. Surgeons tended toward conservative approaches when treating injuries of the distal upper extremity (hand and wrist) and the proximal lower extremity (thigh region).

The merits of doing an operation primarily or secondarily were argued throughout the war. A handbook used by Union medical officers stated that primary operations were performed anytime from time of injury to the occurrence of fever or swelling, approximately forty-eight to sixty hours. The intermediate period was defined as that period during fever and inflammation. Secondary operations were defined as operations performed after fever and constitutional symptoms set in. Surgery was not recommended in the presence of shock.[15] Major operations were to be performed within twenty-four to forty-eight hours from injury, before the "irritive stage" of infection. This time period was often ignored because of the large numbers of casualties and the delays in battlefield evacuation. Usually, a soldier was allowed to rally if he was in shock; occasionally this was accomplished with liquor.[4] Amputation was thought to achieve best results if done as soon as possible after injury or as a necessity in the face of dangerous hemorrhage.[14] Confederate results early in the war agreed with this premise [see Table 2]. Excisional surgery was felt to have better results if done as a secondary procedure.[16] These conclusions were formed on the basis of anecdotal evidence rather than controlled studies. Frank Hastings Hamilton, commenting on the results of primary versus secondary surgery during the war, wrote, "In all secondary amputations and resections...conservative treatment had been tried and failed, and the deaths which followed ought in justice to be charged to conservatism and not to the operation."[17]

Much was written on wound care, and the information provided during the war showed physicians adhered to the miasmatic rather than bacterial theory of infection. Nearly all wounds were "probed," not only to find the projectile but to define the extent of the injury. Clothing, bullets, or shell fragments were removed from wounds. Secondary to this probing, contamination of all wounds occurred. This makes it impossible to compare infection rates and mortality between various treatment techniques. Sometimes wounds were cleaned with solutions that had mild antiseptic qualities such as bromine. The use of ligatures, rather than tourniquets, to stop major vessel hemorrhage was soon practiced by all surgeons and was a major advancement during the war. Nearly all wounds became infected, and white, creamy "laudable" pus was felt to be a good prognostic sign and part of the normal healing process. Wounds that healed without suppuration were essentially considered abnormal and were reported as curiosities.[18,19]

Dressings were usually kept wet. Unfortunately, some dressings were reused and infrequently washed, which led to a dramatic spread of infections.[4] Ice was a valuable adjuvant to the cold water dressings and was even supplied in the heat of July following Gettysburg by the United States Sanitary Commission. Suppurating wounds were sometimes treated with a dilute chlorinated soda called Labarraque's solution, a forerunner of Dakin's solution, a commonly used antiseptic.[18]

Surgical infections were the leading cause of death after surgery. Tetanus, pyemia, erysipelas, and especially gangrene were feared by patient and doctor alike. Various antiseptic agents were tried. Middleton Goldsmith's study of washing wounds with bromine instead of nitric acid in cases of gangrene was a major achievement in the treatment of gangrene during the war. The number of cases of erysipelas were reduced in a Louisville hospital by spraying bromine vapor in the hospital wards.[4] Other antiseptic agents used included potassium permanganate, sodium hypochlorite (Dakin's solution), iodine, and creosote. Four years before Lister's research, carbolic acid was sporadically employed but with mixed results. The problem with the use of these agents was that they were utilized at the wrong time, usually when an infection was in full bloom. Men were further ravaged by disease and malnutrition. J.S. Billings, writing on the operation of excising a hip joint, conceded: "Operating, as I did, upon men whose vital force had been diminished by scorbutus and malaria, and exhausted by transfer from a distance, I had little hope of successful results."[20]

Osteomyelitis was treated somewhat differently by the opposing sides. Both sides used cold compresses, local debridement, drainage, and amputation to treat bone infections. However, a unique form of treatment was developed serendipitously by the South during the war. A group of Confederate surgeons, imprisoned in Chattanooga, had been denied supplies to keep their men's wounds clean. Subsequently, maggots infested the wounds and, surprisingly, cases of osteomyelitis and gangrene were cured. After their release, the surgeons applied this method in Southern hospitals, which led to improved results.[1,4,21] The North continued to have poor responses to treatment because they scrupulously eliminated all maggots from their soldiers' wounds. Maggot treatment was eventually rediscovered. Maggots bred under sterile conditions were used to treat osteomyelitis during World War I and were reported to have excellent results in studies by Baer and Eastman.[21]

As mentioned earlier, most wounds involved the extremities [see Table 3]. Of those killed in action on the battlefield, 94% had head, neck, chest, or abdominal wounds, while only 6% had isolated extremity wounds.[4] Thus, extremity injuries provided the majority of a surgeon's experience. In addition, the vast majority of the injuries were caused by small-arms fire. The dramatized Hollywood frontal charge involving bayonets and sabres occurred infrequently and was responsible for only 0.37% of all injuries. Accordingly, despite widespread use on both sides, cannon and mortar fire was responsible for only a small percentage of the wounds encountered. One medical officer reported anecdotally that while 250 cannon were present on both sides at the Battle of the Wilderness, only twelve injuries could be attributed to shells.[4]

Information on treatment of various orthopaedic injuries is available in the six-volume set *The Medical and Surgical History of the War of the Rebellion,* compiled after the war by medical officers. It contains thousands of case reports and statistics on soldier wounds and their treatments. The statistical reports are by necessity incomplete and it is difficult to make strict

Table 3.
Relative Frequency of Anatomic Locations of Gunshot Wounds [2]

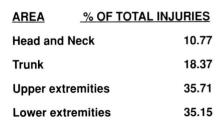

AREA	% OF TOTAL INJURIES
Head and Neck	10.77
Trunk	18.37
Upper extremities	35.71
Lower extremities	35.15

comparisons of the various treatments for a given wound or region. The editors of this work evidently also realized this: "…[the results of mortality] show a percentage highly flattering to the efforts of conservation; but it must be borne in mind that the cases reported as treated conservatively were cases selected as specially adapted to this mode of treatment, and probably were the least serious."[2] Nevertheless, this incredible work and compilation of statistics shed light upon the decision-making process that most surgeons faced. It also documents the success obtained based upon type of treatment for various anatomic locations. Many detailed case reports describe the surgical procedures and postoperative treatment administered. Because the bulk of surgical descriptions and case reports are compiled in this one source, any review of orthopaedic treatment during the war must rely heavily upon *The Medical and Surgical History* as a reference. It is written from the Union perspective. Confederate reports are only partially available since the majority of medical documents were lost in the fire that engulfed Richmond near the close of the war.

Only injuries involving fractures and orthopaedic treatment will be reviewed in this text. The timing of surgical procedures generally conforms to the following pattern of time elapsed since injury: primary—zero to three days; intermediate—four to thirty days; secondary—greater than thirty days. Some variability in this pattern is encountered in regard to amputations: primary hip disarticulation—less than twenty-four hours; other primary amputations—zero to forty-eight hours; intermediate—three to thirty days, secondary—greater than thirty days. Also included are photographs and case reports shown as examples of soldier injuries and treatment at various anatomic levels. These are from another monumental work compiled by George Otis, the fourth Surgeon General of the United States: *Photographs of Surgical Cases and Specimens.*

A soldier undergoes Buck's traction, a method of traction wherein force is applied in line with the leg.

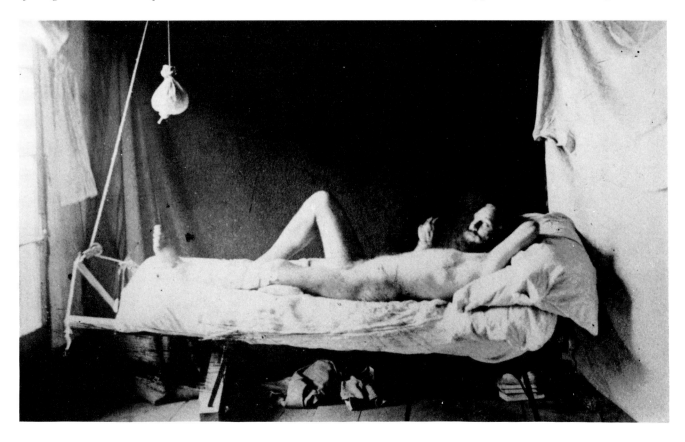

IV.

Spine

Table 4.
Summary of
Mortality from
Gunshot Wounds to
the Spine [2]

There were more than 600 cases of recorded spine injuries during the war [see Table 4]. Surgeries upon the spine were regarded as "operative interference" and the surgeries performed were very limited in nature. No instances of formal trephination were reported. Operations included ball removal (thirty-four cases) and bone removal (twenty-four cases). The overall surgical mortality rate was 43%. Wounds of the spine were looked upon pessimistically since results were dismal except in cases that had relatively little true spinal involvement (i.e., only a spinous process without spinal cord injury). One lucky private survived a remarkable gunshot wound to the neck. W.W. Keen, considered the father of American neurosurgery, described the private's wound this way: "Nearly the entire body of the third cervical vertebra has come away, including the anterior half of the transverse process and the vertebral foramen....What supports his head anteriorly, I can't conceive...."[2] Surprisingly, this soldier recovered enough to work as a hospital attendant afterward with only residual paralysis of his right arm.

REGION	NUMBER	% MORTALITY
Cervical	91	70.0
Thoracic	137	63.5
Lumbar	149	45.5
Cervical/Thoracic	2	50.0
Thoracic/Lumbar	3	100.0
Unknown	260	51.3
Total / Overall	642	55.5

𝔖𝔲𝔯𝔤𝔢𝔬𝔫 𝔊𝔢𝔫𝔢𝔯𝔞𝔩'𝔰 𝔒𝔣𝔣𝔦𝔠𝔢
ARMY MEDICAL MUSEUM

Photograph No. 2. *Second, Third, and Fourth Lumbar Vertebræ, with a Conoidal Ball imbedded in the Left Side of the Body of the Third Lumbar Vertebra*

Private Thomas Durning, Co. F, 1st Michigan Sharpshooters, age nineteen years, was wounded, June 26, 1864, and admitted into Stanton U.S. General Hospital, Washington July 1, 1864. An elongated musket ball, entering the loins just above the crest of the left ilium, buried itself in the body of the third lumbar vertebra, carrying with it a portion of the man's blouse. On July 4th, symptoms of tetanus appeared, which became rapidly of the gravest nature, and the case terminated fatally on the next day, July 5, 1864. The specimen was contributed by Assistant Surgeon George A. Mursick, U.S. Vols.

Photographed at the Army Medical Museum.

By Order of the Surgeon General:

GEORGE A. OTIS,
Bv't Lt. Col. and Ass't Surg. U.S.A., Curator, A.M.M.

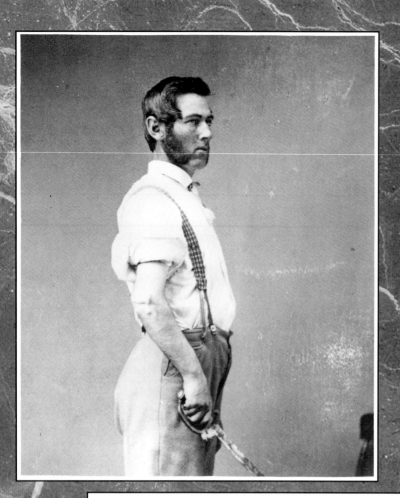

Surgeon General's Office

ARMY MEDICAL MUSEUM

Photograph No. 54. *Case of successful excision of the right elbow-joint for gunshot injury.*

Private W.T. Riley, D, 86th New York, Age 21 was accidentally wounded at Brandy Station November 26, 1863 by a musket ball which shattered the inner-condyle of the right humerus and the olecranon process of the ulna. He was admitted to the Mansion House Hospital the same day, having bled quite largely on the way. On December 19th, 1863 surgeon Charles Page, USA, excised the elbow joint employing the "H-shaped" incision. Two and a half inches of the lower extremity of the humerus, an inch of the upper extremity of the ulna and a small portion of the head of radius were removed. The case progressed most favorably and in May, 1864 Riley went to his home on furlough with a useful arm. He was subsequently discharged from service. In 1865 he re-enlisted in Company K 5th regiment, First Army Corps, with the approval of Lieutenant Colonel Dougherty, Medical Director of the Corps. "The man went through the manual before me," Surgeon Dougherty writes, "And stated his readiness to do all the duties of a soldier. He wished it recorded that he was competent and prepared in order that during the term of his service he might be held to full duty. The degree of motion was perhaps one third of the normal amount." This photograph was taken in June, 1865. Riley was pensioned and his disability rated as total, third grade. He was paid March 4, 1874.

Photographed at the Army Medical Museum.

By order of the Surgeon General:

GEORGE A. OTIS
Assistant Surgeon, U.S.A., Curator, A.M.M.

V.

Upper Extremity

Valuable information about treatment of upper extremity injuries was gained.

The overall mortality rate for upper extremity injuries was 6.5%.[2] Surgical intervention became more conservative as the war continued since results of more conservative treatment and surgical resection were favorable compared to more aggressive amputations. Confederate surgeon Dr. Felix Formento was adamant about conserving the upper extremity at all costs. He performed a number of excisions himself, maintaining the limb in a functional position by appropriate splinting and then utilizing physical therapy to allow a return to function.[23] Functional outcomes were important and attempts to compare the long-term outcome with surgical procedure were made through follow-up reports by military pension examiners. Unfortunately, these reports tended to overrate disability so that the pensioning soldier could receive the largest allowance entitled under the law. "This is especially true in regard to the results of the excisions of joints, many men being returned as more or less unfit to follow their callings, although they have fairly useful limbs."[2] Valuable information regarding treatment of upper extremity injuries was gained. Based on statistics gleaned from the war, Hamilton wrote in *Practical Treatise on Fractures and Dislocations:* "In general it may be stated that gunshot fractures of the upper extremities do not demand amputation, and that similar injuries in the lower extremities do demand amputation....[Excisions of the upper extremity] will in most cases eventually unite, and give the patients tolerably useful limbs."[17]

VI.

Clabicle and Scapula

Of 2,280 isolated clavicle and scapula gunshot wounds, 314 deaths were recorded. About 50% of the injured were unable to return to duty afterward. Injuries to the left side were 4% more common,[2] possibly because the left side is more exposed when firing a rifle. Conservative treatment was favored and a pocket medical manual recommended using a Velpeau sling for transportation of soldiers with clavicle fractures.[24] A type of abduction pillow placed in the axilla served as a way of treating clavicle fractures. Surgery was generally limited to excision of portions of the clavicle and scapula. There is only one case of a soldier who had a complete excision of the scapula secondary to a grapeshot injury, the war's version of a shrapnel injury. This resulted in an atrophied and useless arm.[25]

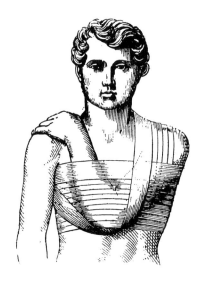

The Velpeau sling.

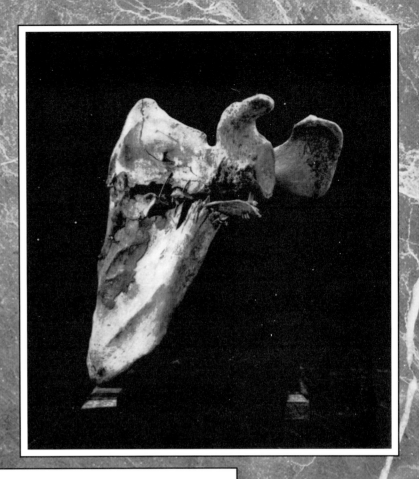

𝔖𝔲𝔯𝔤𝔢𝔬𝔫 𝔊𝔢𝔫𝔢𝔯𝔞𝔩'𝔰 𝔒𝔣𝔣𝔦𝔠𝔢

ARMY MEDICAL MUSEUM

Photograph No. 86. *Left scapula showing a gunshot fracture nearly parallel with the spine of the scapula with two fragments of a conoidal musket ball.*

Private William Fuller, F, 18th Massachusetts, age thirty, was wounded at the second battle of Bull Run, August 30, 1862 by a conoidal musket ball which entered to the left of the spinal column, and passing outwards, traversed the body of the scapula and the muscles of the upper part of the arm. The patient was conveyed to Union Chapel Hospital at Alexandria, Virginia. On the 3rd and again on the 5th of September, misshapen pieces of ball and few fragments of bone were extracted through an incision on the outer edges of the scapula. On September 19th, symptoms of purulent infection were manifested. An active treatment by stimulants, quinine, iron and ammonia were instituted, but unavailing, and on September 25th, 1862, the case terminated fatally. At the autopsy, a large collection of extravasated blood was found beneath the scapula and between the muscles of the shoulder. There was extensive serous effusion in the left pleural cavity and numerous metastasis foci in both lungs. The scapula is numbered specimen 188, in the museum collection. Full notes of the case were forwarded by Acting Assistant Surgeon W.H. Butler. See *First Surgical Volume of the Medical and Surgical History of the Rebellion*, p. 476.

Photographed at the Army Medical Museum.

By order of the Surgeon General:

GEORGE A. OTIS
Assistant Surgeon, U.S.A., Curator, A.M.M.

𝖘𝖚𝖗𝖌𝖊𝖔𝖓 𝕲𝖊𝖓𝖊𝖗𝖆𝖑'𝖘 𝕺𝖋𝖋𝖎𝖈𝖊
ARMY MEDICAL MUSEUM

Photograph series, No. 146. *Successful intermediate excision of the head and three inches of the shaft of the right humerus for gunshot fracture.*

Private Samuel D. Tineker, Company D., 14th Indiana Volunteers, was wounded in the battle of Wilderness, May 6, 1864, by a musket ball which entered the posterior surface of the right humerus and past forwards, making its exit at the anterior surface, fracturing the head of the humerus and the anterior and posterior borders of the glenoid cavity. On May 30th he was admitted to Lincoln Hospital, Washington, D.C., and on June 1st was etherized, and the head and three inches of the shaft of the humerus were excised by surgeon J.C. McKee, U.S.A., through a straight incision commencing at the coracoid process of the clavicle and extending downward five inches. On October 10th, 1864, the parts were entirely healed. The patient was subsequently transferred to the soldier's home and discharged from the service of the United States.

Photographed at the Army Medical Museum.

By order of the Surgeon General:

GEORGE A. OTIS
Asst. Surg., U.S.A., Curator, A.M.M.

VII.

Shoulder

Of those gunshot fractures of the shoulder that were treated by expectation, about 25% died and 25% were able to return to duty.[2] Reports show that in addition to dressings for wounds, treatment also consisted of passive motion or bandaging the arm to the chest, a trial of various splints, or an abduction pillow that kept the arm out from the chest. These splints also applied traction to the upper arm. There is evidence that the Confederate surgeons did not trust the results of expectant treatment, with regard to the shoulder, and resorted to excision and amputation more frequently.[26] The conclusion of treatment methods after the war was summarized as: "While the naked statistics present the expectant method of dealing with shot injuries at the shoulder in a somewhat favorable light, a survey of the individual cases fails to increase our confidence in this mode of treatment."[2]

Shoulder resection arthroplasty was the best hope for saving the limb and restoring function. Similar to scapular trauma, injuries were more common to the left side than the right side secondary to the exposed position of the left shoulder in firing position among the infantry. One cavalry officer reported that in cavalry troops injuries to the right side predominated since the right arm would be exposed when the sabre or pistol was raised. Shoulder excision had been performed just twelve times before the war and only in fixed hospitals. During the war, shoulder excision was commonly performed on the field. Medical manuals instructed: "Excisions of the large joints are never to be practiced on the battle-field, or under conditions which require the immediate transportation of the wounded...Exceptions to this rule may be made for excisions of the upper extremity..."[16] The excisions included removal of part of the humeral head, shaft, clavicle, or scapula. Common incisions made were: longitudinal, most frequently done anteriorly—Langenbeck's approach; V- or U-shaped, and, rarely, transverse incisions. The biceps tendon was preserved when possible. Postoperatively, the axilla was padded to counteract the pull of the teres major and latissimus

Injuries were more common to the left side due to the exposed position of the body of an infantryman when in firing position.

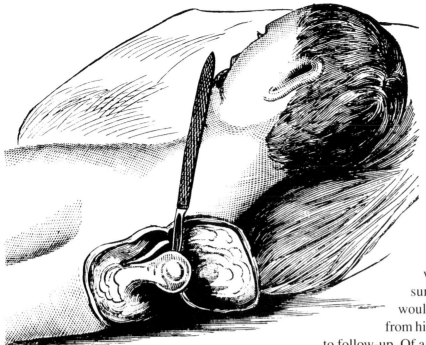

A shoulder resection being performed through a U-shaped incision.

dorsi muscles of the back. A patient would be initially placed in a sling and passive motion started as soon as possible.[16]

Of the more than 1,086 surgical cases reported, only fourteen required eventual amputation [see Tables 5 and 6]. One patient, a Confederate prisoner who had undergone an extensive excision arthroplasty encompassing his humeral head, proximal shaft, coracoid, and acromial processes, scapular spine, and a portion of the glenoid shoulder cavity, felt the result was excellent. He later wrote: "A complete success. I am writing with the arm, a masterpiece of surgical skill." He feared that his result would not be known since he had escaped from his prison during the war and had been lost to follow-up. Of a small series of nine excisions examined after the war, two had "serviceable arms" while seven had "useless arms."

The typical course is displayed by the following pension reports of a private who underwent an excision arthroplasty of the shoulder. Initially, "This officer can use his arm at [a] table, and plays well on the banjo." As the stiffness of his joint increased, his function was described as "Cannot raise the arm...Has little use of his hand." This report may have been an exaggeration of disability (as was often done by pension examiners) since, interestingly, the patient later studied medicine and became a practicing physician. Another case earlier reported that the soldier's "arm is useful, the patient can feed himself, and take his hat off." Later, it was reported that "...he is not able to make use of the right arm and hand." A Confederate prisoner wounded at Gettysburg who had an excision reported six years later to the Union surgeon: "When I think of the strength and use of my arm, I feel under many obligations to you; for I have been told that you contended the operation, while others opposed it and were in favor of cutting the arm off at the shoulder. I use it to good advantage in ploughing, hoeing, and cutting with an axe...I find a greater difficulty in striking or nailing overhead..." The loss of abduction after the procedure as seen by these case reports was almost universal due to damage or excision of the rotator cuff and loss of deltoid muscle function. The frequency of excisions increased as the war continued because of the apparent short-term successes.[2]

Shoulder amputations were resorted to less frequently than excisions but had slightly lower mortality rates [see Table 7]. Amputation was done not only for fractures involving the shoulder but occasionally for comminuted fractures of the diaphysis or proximal portion of the bone. Occasionally, portions of the scapula and clavicle were also removed. Usually a large deltoid shoulder flap was used for coverage. Occasionally an anterior/posterior flap was employed.

TYPE	NUMBER	% MORTALITY
Primary	515	31.06
Intermediate	224	46.4
Secondary	92	29.3
Total	831	35.0

Table 5. Mortality for Operations of Excision of Shoulder Joint, Union [2]

TYPE	NUMBER	% MORTALITY
Primary	41	31.7
Secondary	27	25.9

Table 6. Mortality for Operations of Excision of Shoulder Joint, Confederate [2]

TYPE	NUMBER	% MORTALITY, US	% MORTALITY, CS
Primary	499	24.1	31
Intermediary	157	45.8	N/A
Secondary	66	28.7	71
Unspecified	130	23.5	N/A
Total / Overall	852	28.5	N/A

Table 7. Mortality of Shoulder Amputation Cases [2,46]

TREATMENT	NUMBER	% MORTALITY
Expectation	3005	15.2
Amputation	3685	22.5
Excision	632	27.1

Table 8. Mortality of Treatments for Humerus Fractures [2]

VIII.
Arm

Treatment of humeral fractures from gunshot wounds generally required amputation or conservative measures [see Table 8, previous page]. Conservative management consisted of bandaging the injured arm to the chest or utilizing various splints that provided traction at the fracture site. The type of treatment was "an argument of necessity as well as choice, and limbs that in happier circumstances might have been preserved, had often, in a flying army or a dangerous campaign, to be cut off...it is less dreadful to be dragged along with a neat amputated stump than a swollen and fractured limb, where the arteries are in constant danger from the splintered bones."[2] Stonewall Jackson underwent an amputation through the proximal humerus because of a gunshot wound he accidentally received at the hands of his own men at Chancellorsville. He survived the surgery only to die of pneumonia several days later.

The first attempt at open reduction-internal fixation for a gunshot fracture of the humerus occurred during the war, with four such cases recorded. Three of them were performed by Dr. Benjamin Howard. His method was to resect the comminuted ends of the fracture site, place the ends in opposition, and use a special drill and suture passer to hold the bone ends together using a wire. He actually performed them on the field and felt there was a great advantage in being able to transport the patient with a relatively stable fracture site.[27] His methods were largely condemned by other surgeons who feared the placement of a foreign body into a wound. Three of the four patients survived the procedure, and pension reports stated that the fractures had healed, but all three patients had limited shoulder mobility and limited limb use.[2]

Sketch of an open reduction-internal fixation method, in which a wire was used to hold the fractured bone fragments together.

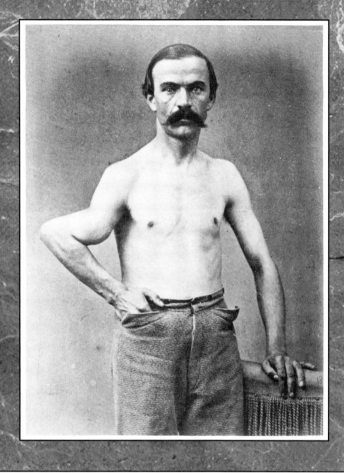

Surgeon General's Office

ARMY MEDICAL MUSEUM

Photograph No. 189.

Private Jacob Eggerstedt, McRae's Battery, was wounded at the Battle of Valverde, New Mexico February 21st, 1862 by a ball which fractured his right humerus. The arm was put in splints, there was no comminution to warrant an operation for the extraction of fragments or resection. The patient recovered from the injury; but with pseudoarthrosis. He visited the museum in the summer of 1867, and his photograph was taken.

Photographed at the Army Medical Museum.

By order of the Surgeon General:

GEORGE A. OTIS
Bv't Lt. Col., Ass't Surg., U.S.A., Curator, A.M.M.

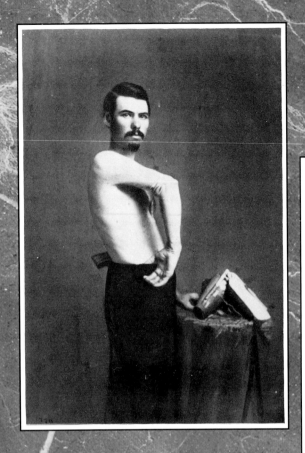

Surgeon General's Office
ARMY MEDICAL MUSEUM

Photograph No. 280. *Successful excision of the elbow-joint for gunshot injury.*

J.T. Hertzog, a private of Company K, 4th Pennsylvania Volunteers, a German of remarkably temperate habits, having never used stimulants, tobacco, tea nor coffee, and of excellent constitution, was wounded at the Battle of Pocotaligo, October 22, 1862, by a ball which entered the right elbow joint at the outer and emerged just above the inner condyle of the humerus at the opposite side. He was admitted to Hospital #1 Beaufort, South Carolina, on October 24th. Two days subsequently the lower end of the humerus with the articulating ends of the ulna and radius were excised by Surgeon R.B. Bontecou, U.S.V., and the arm laid upon an angular splint of two parallel strips leaving an open space the whole extent, thus facilitating approach to the wound of exit. Morphine was applied to the wound, it was covered with cerate cloth and bags of ice were directed to be kept applied. By November 1, suppuration was considerable but the tumefaction of the arm and forearm was much diminished. The lead wire sutures were removed on November 15, the wound having healed sufficiently to keep the parts in shape. On December 1st, the wound had nearly closed, there being but a slight discharge; the general condition of the patient was good and he sat up to take his food. Some days previous to December 15th, the patient had been walking about the hospital grounds, the wound was nearly healed and the elbow joint presented free mobility in every direction. On December 28, he was transferred north, the wound being healed. The excised portions of bone with the history were presented to the museum by the operator, and are No. 2023 of the surgical section. The man was discharged from the service February 24, 1863, and pensioned. On March 18, 1863, pension examiner Lewellyn Beaver reports "an open running sore." In June, 1864, Dr. Bontecou writes that he saw his patient at Fort Wood, New York Harbor, in July, 1863, and that he had good motion of the elbow. Another report from pension examiner Beaver dated September 11, 1866, states that this man had completely lost the use of his arm. There was four inches shortening. He rated his disability total.

Photographed at the Army Medical Museum.

By order of the Surgeon General:

GEORGE A. OTIS
Ass't Surg., U.S.A., Curator, A.M.M.

IX.

Elbow

Conservative treatment of elbow gunshot wounds utilized various right-angle splints. In contrast to the shoulders, bony ankylosis and fusion did occur. Conservative treatment, while having the lowest mortality rate of all elbow treatments [see Table 9], generally resulted in a poor functional outcome: "The known instances of recovery with preservation of the functions of the joint are very few; and those with ankylosis in a favorable position, with freedom from disease about the joint and good use of the forearm and hand, were not numerous."[2]

Elbow excision arthroplasty was considered the most successful of all resection procedures done during the war. A single longitudinal incision was the most common surgical approach, along the radial border, or thumb side, of the ulnar nerve. The longitudinal incision was recommended over a transverse incision so that splitting, rather than cutting, of the triceps muscle would help to preserve the insertion site to maintain forearm extension. Full excision was considered more functionally sound than partial excision, having a better functional prognosis. Postoperative treatment included placing the arm on a pillow at 45° or using a suspension splint. Cold water dressings were applied and passive motion started as soon as possible.[16] The function of the hand was often preserved. Reports of good functional recovery were numerous.[28] One report stated that: the patient "can hold the fork firmly in carving at the table, and says the arm is invaluable." One soldier wrote, "I can write as well as ever but experience some difficulty in raising my arm."[2]

Elbow amputations were uncommon. A disproportionate number of these procedures were carried out for injuries caused by large projectiles that had destroyed the forearm. Another common mechanism of injury was premature explosion of a large gun when the artilleryman was ramming a cartridge and his forearm was pulpified. Of thirty-nine cases, the mortality rate was 7.6%. Five had to have reamputation at a more proximal level. Some surgeons felt that the forearm stump was not as well suited for a prosthesis as with a more proximal amputation.

Table 9. Results of Treatments of Shot Fractures to the Elbow [2]

TREATMENT	#	RTD	%MORT.
Expectation	938	285	10.3
Excision	529*	80	22.4
Amputation	1124~	109	24.3

RTD=Return to duty.

*64 required eventual above-elbow amputation.

~17 required eventual amputation at shoulder.

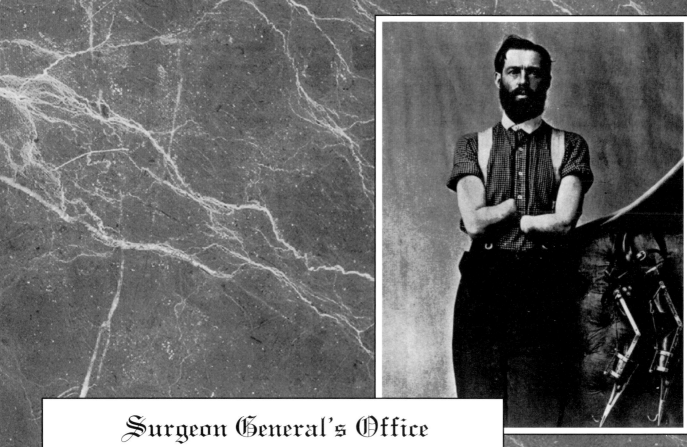

Surgeon General's Office
ARMY MEDICAL MUSEUM

Photograph No. 205. *Double amputation of the forearms for injury caused by the premature explosion of a gun.*

Private Samuel H. Decker, Company I, 4th US Artillery, while ramming his piece at the Battle of Perryville, Kentucky, October 8, 1862, had half of his right forearm and somewhat less of the left blown off by the premature explosion of the gun. At the same time his face and chest were badly burned. Five hours after the accident, both forearms were amputated by the circular method about the middle, by an assistant surgeon of the regular army whose name he cannot recall. He laid in the field hospital at Perryville until the wounds were partially cicatrized when on November 1 he went to Louisville, Kentucky and, on the 3rd of November, 1862, he was discharged to service. About the middle of January, 1863, the stumps were completely healed. In the Autumn of 1864, Mr. Decker began to make experiments for providing himself with artificial limbs. He produced, in March, 1865, an apparatus hereto unrivaled for its ingenuity and utility. He receives a pension of $300 per year and is a door keeper at the House of Representatives. On November 29, 1867, Mr. Decker visited the Army Medical Museum where a number of photographs of his stumps were made. With the aid of his ingenious apparatus he is able to write legibly, to pick up any small objects, a pin for example, to carry packages of ordinary weight, to feed and clothe himself, and in one or two instances of disorder in the congressional gallery has proved himself a formidable police officer.

Photographed at the Army Medical Museum.

By order of the Surgeon General:

GEORGE A. OTIS
Bv't Lt. Col., Ass't Surg., U.S.A., Curator, A.M.M.

X.

Forearm

As with the humerus, conservative treatment and amputation were resorted to far more frequently than excision. There appears to have been poor results in terms of function following excision alone. It was felt that amputations had an unacceptably high mortality rate [see Table 10] and should have been done only if there was severe soft tissue loss or both arteries were severed. Many were done unnecessarily for open fractures. This slowly became apparent as the war continued, after the realization that the results were more acceptable with conservative treatment. Thus, the rate of amputation for these injuries was much less in the second half of the war. Confederate mortality figures were even higher, and was likely due to a higher amputation rate.[29] Postoperative splinting and physical therapy became used more frequently with the recognition that splinting the forearm in neutral rotation, without twisting at the elbow or wrist, provided the best chance of a good, functional recovery.[30]

Table 10.
Mortality from Treatments of Forearm Fractures from Gunshot Wounds [2]

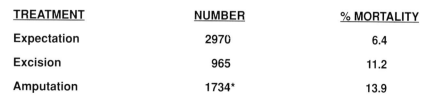

TREATMENT	NUMBER	% MORTALITY
Expectation	2970	6.4
Excision	965	11.2
Amputation	1734*	13.9

* eight cases were bilateral amputations

XI.

Wrist

Table 11.
Results of Treatments of Gunshot Wounds of the Wrist [2]

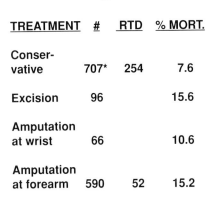

TREATMENT	#	RTD	% MORT.
Conservative	707*	254	7.6
Excision	96		15.6
Amputation at wrist	66		10.6
Amputation at forearm	590	52	15.2

* Includes cases that may have gone on to eventual surgery.

RTD = returned to duty

Conservative treatment was more successful in those cases in which the bullet had passed in the anterior to posterior direction rather than transversely or across the wrist from side to side, which caused more bone destruction. Most wrists treated non-operatively were described as ankylosed. Hamilton, in a manual written from experiences of the war, recommended the avoidance of compressive dressings and advocated early passive motion to try to prevent the frequent problem of wrist stiffness. He also recommended that the fingers should be actively flexed and extended frequently.[31]

Wrist excisions had disappointing results when compared to shoulder and elbow excisions. Postoperatively the fingers and thumb were placed around a roller bandage or ball in a functional position and passive motion begun as soon as possible.[16] Six total wrist resections were performed and this group of patients were found to have better results than patients undergoing amputation. Because of such small patient numbers, results were difficult to evaluate and ranged from "can use the hand for a great variety of purposes, in eating, dressing, and seizing light objects" to the more common "useless hand."[2] Resections of the ulna were noted to result in more deformity and neurologic defects than resections of the radius. One series showed only nine of sixty-eight hands had good functional results. There was too much variability in the types of surgery performed to deduce surgical guidelines delineating specific indications for a given wrist excision.[2] It is interesting to note that amputations of the forearm for gunshot wounds of the wrist had a higher mortality than similar amputations for gunshot wounds of the forearm itself [see Table 11]. This theme is seen throughout the war regardless of the location or extremity: mortality was higher for an injury involving a joint than the area immediately more proximal.

Surgeon General's Office
ARMY MEDICAL MUSEUM

Photograph No. 5. *Resection of portions of the carpus and metacarpus, and of the lower extremity of the ulna.*

Major C.W. Hobbs, 7th New York Heavy Artillery, was wounded at Cold Harbor, June 3, 1864, by three musket balls. One inflicted a flesh wound of the left thigh, passing across the popliteal space, close to the hamstring tendons. The second fractured the third and fourth metacarpal bones of the left hand and made its exit near the wrist. The third entered the left hand between the distal extremities of the first and second metacarpals, comminuted the second and third metacarpals, the unciform and the cuneiform bones, and the lower extremity of the ulna and made its exit on the outer side of the forearm. Primary excisions were performed by surgeon J.E. Pomfret, 7th New York Heavy Artillery. Two inches of the distal extremity of the ulna were removed with the fractured bones of the carpus and metacarpus, and three outer fingers. The case progressed without any untoward complication and recovery was complete in two months. The photograph was taken July 7th, 1865. The remaining portion of the radiocarpal articulation was not ankylosed and the movements of the thumb and forefinger were unimpaired. Major Hobbs was pensioned from expiration of his term of service until September 24, 1867, when he reentered the service.

Photographed at the Army Medical Museum.

By order of the Surgeon General:

GEORGE A. OTIS
Assistant Surgeon, U.S.A., Curator, A.M.M.

XII.

Hand

More than 11,000 gunshot wounds of the hand were recorded, of which the majority received various amputations of the fingers with or without metacarpal hand amputation. More than a quarter of those injured were treated conservatively, with an overall mortality rate for all treatments of 3.1%.[2] Shot injuries of the hand, as well as fractures from other causes were quite common. Even General Robert E. Lee sustained a "small bone" fracture, possibly a metacarpal fracture, in one of his hands that required splinting before the Battle of Antietam.[32] Palmar splints were used commonly for both gunshot wounds and closed fractures. Physicians were advised to splint metacarpal or phalangeal fractures in a hand splint or to close the hand over a ball of the proper size and hold it in place with adhesive plaster.[33] There was great emphasis on saving the thumb, even in the very worst cases. Disarticulation, or excision of the digit at a joint, of the finger was found to be preferable to dividing it in the mid-portion.[14]

A sidebar:
Amputation

In a skilled surgeon's hands, an amputation must follow various rules and procedures to be successful. There are two competing concerns: the surgeon must strive to preserve as much length as possible but must remove as much of the limb as necessary to eliminate destroyed tissue that could lead to a poorly formed stump or even endanger the soldier's life. With these two competing concerns in mind, the Civil War surgeon had to make a determination of the level of injury based on visual demarcation of viable vs. nonviable tissue, as well as any concommitant fractures. The surgeon would often explore the wound with his finger or use various probes if visual inspection was not definitive. The same instruments were used on consecutive cases, even from infected wounds, without any cleaning of the instruments or their hands between cases. This was especially true in the field hospitals where the case load was high and water scarce. Once the level of amputation that would be expected to heal was established, the patient was anesthetized and the procedure commenced. If the amputation was far enough from the trunk, a tourniquet was used. The goal, after saving the soldier's life, in lower extremity amputation surgery, was to provide a stump that would accommodate a prosthesis readily without pain or skin breakdown.

The circular and flap methods of amputation were the most common types used during the war. Both methods had their advocates and advantages. The circular method was easier to dress, easier to transport, and had fewer cases of secondary hemorrhage, although this was debatable. The surgeon would start the circular amputation by dividing the skin and subcutaneous tissues down to the level of the muscles.

The skin would be retracted proximally, much like rolling up the cuff of a shirt sleeve, and the muscle would be divided circularly at the highest level possible. This was followed by cutting the bone at this level with a saw. Arteries and large veins were identified and drawn distal with a forceps where they could be tied with a ligature made of silk or cotton. The large nerves were also pulled out as far as possible and cut sharply allowing the stump of the nerve to retract back into the soft tissues of the stump.

The advantage of the flap method was the speed in which it could be performed. It was also easier to obtain adequate soft tissue coverage for the bone with this method. The flap method differed in the way the soft tissues were divided. The arteries, veins, and nerves were handled identically to the circular method. One method created flaps by placing the amputation knife directly down to bone allowing it to "skid" over the top of the bone and out the other side of the limb. At this point, the knife could be drawn out away from the body and outward creating one of the two flaps. The same motion would then be performed on the opposite side of the limb to create the other flap.

At this point, regardless of the method used, the end of the bone was smoothed with bone biting forceps, rongeur type instruments, and rasps. The skin, if the circular method was used, or the flaps of muscle and skin could be brought together and loosely sutured with silk or wire sutures. Some surgeons preferred to leave the wound open. The stump would be dressed and sometimes supported in starch or plaster splints to limit the amount of motion over the end of the bone. Opium and whiskey were employed for postoperative pain management.

Photograph No. 156. *Recovery without an operation after gunshot fracture involving the right acetabulum and head of the femur.*

Lieutenant James C. Strong, 38th New York Volunteers was wounded at the battle of Williamsburg, Virginia May 6, 1862, by a conoidal musket ball which entered over the right sartorius muscle about four inches below its origin and made its exit near the right margin of the lower portion of the sacrum. Surgeon A.J. Berry, 38th New York Volunteers, examined the wound and found that the ball had deeply grooved the head of the femur and had fractured the upper rim of the acetabulum. A detached fragment of the rim nearly one and one-half inches in length, a part of it covered with articulate cartilage, together with portions of clothing, were extracted from the wound. On May 8 the patient was transferred by a steamer from Queen's Creek Landing to the Hygeia Hospital at Fort Monroe. Here he remained until the 13th when he undertook a painful journey on a litter and reached his home in Buffalo New York. The injured limb was semi-flexed and rotated inwards, the head of the femur being dislocated upon the dorsum of the ileum. Any attempt to place the limb in position produced such acute suffering that the effort was abandoned. For ten weeks there was profuse suppuration with burrowing of pus in the thigh and intense pain with chills, profuse perspiration and great prostration after which a very gradual amendment took place. On December 12, 1862, the patient was removed to Philadelphia and entered at the officer's hospital at Cammack's Woods where he was able to bear treatment by Buck's method of extension by weights. Here a number of spicula of bone were extracted or washed from the wound. On January 6, 1863, the patient was discharged from hospital. On June 1 the wounds were nearly closed and he rejoined his regiment on crutches, and was mustered out with the regiment on June 22, 1863. On September 29 he was appointed Colonel in the Veteran Reserve Corps. He was subsequently brevetted Brigadier General. In July, 1866, when the photograph was taken, General Strong was in good health. His limb was shortened nearly five inches; but by the inclination of the pelvis and extension of the toes, he was able to walk with surprising ease and activity with or without a cane. The head of the femur was firmly ankylosed on the dorsum of the ileum. The cicatrices appeared sound.

Photographed at the Army Medical Museum.
By order of the Surgeon General:

GEORGE A. OTIS
Bv't Lt. Col., Ass't Surgeon, U.S.A., Curator, A.M.M.

XIII.

Pelvis

Pelvic gunshot wounds had an overall mortality of 36.4%, even for injuries that did not involve the internal pelvic contents. Injuries to the sacrum and coccyx were attended with the highest mortality rates. The left ilium was injured 10% more than the right "notwithstanding the partial protection afforded by the canteen, haversack, and side arms." This predominance of left-sided injuries is attributed to the more exposed position of the left side when firing a rifle.

Operations were generally limited to excisions of portions of the ilium or other sequestered loose pieces of bone. Trepanning or making holes in the bone using gouges or special saws helped to enlarge the space in order to remove a bullet or projectile. Mortality was high due to a wide variety of complications: "...in wounds of the pelvis, purulent infiltration, cellulitis with gangrene, urinary infiltration, necrosis with exfoliations and protracted suppurations, paralysis, and pyemia, are the more common causes of death." One fortunate colonel had a successful case of irrigation of a fistula of the pelvis located near the anterior superior iliac spine with a "very dilute solution of carbolic acid. The wound entirely closed and gave him no trouble for two or three years."[2]

Mortality was high due to a wide variety of complications.

XIV.
Lower Extremity

As the incidence of trench warfare increased, lower extremity injuries decreased.

The lower extremity was the second most common site of injury, with an overall mortality rate of 13.8%.[2] Soldiers were sometimes told to fire at the feet of the enemy since wounded men would be a greater liability to the opposing army in terms of mobility. As trench warfare became more common toward the end of the war—such as during the sieges of Petersburg and Mobile—these injuries decreased as a percentage of the whole. Once again, the left extremity was injured about 10% more often than the right. As with upper extremity injuries, approximately two-thirds of the gunshot wounds did not involve fractures. In addition to procedures done for fractures, there were five cases of tenotomies, division of a tendon, done for relief of deformities: three of hamstrings, two of the Achilles.[2] Initially used by Mathysen in Europe and Pirogoff in Russia, plaster of Paris splints were first used on American soldiers during this war for various lower extremity injuries. They were recommended by the U.S. Sanitary Commission for the treatment of fractured limbs during the war in an 1864 publication.[34] Despite this publication, plaster splints were not extensively utilized. Prior to the use of plaster, starched bandages were used but had the disadvantage of taking days to dry. After the swelling had subsided, plaster bandages were applied and openings cut directly over the wounds. It was also thought best to leave a portion of the splint open to allow for swelling. Plaster was especially appropriate for supporting the limb after an excision. Dr. J. Swan, under General George B. McClellan during the Seven Days' Battle, employed the use of plaster splints to help transport several soldiers with fractures back to Washington. Conversely, there is very little mention of the use of plaster for upper extremity injuries.

𝔖𝔲𝔯𝔤𝔢𝔬𝔫 𝔊𝔢𝔫𝔢𝔯𝔞𝔩'𝔰 𝔒𝔣𝔣𝔦𝔠𝔢

ARMY MEDICAL MUSEUM

Photograph No. 199-200. *Successful secondary amputation of the knee joint.*

Corporal David D. Cole, A, Second New York Cavalry, age 23, was wounded at Amelia Courthouse Virginia, April 7, 1865, by a conoidal musket ball which passed through the left leg. It was thought the tibia and fibula were uninjured. He was admitted to Hick's Hospital, Baltimore, on June 28. The tibia had become bare for nearly its whole length, the limb was much tumefied and inner muscular spaces were filled with pus. On August 1st, 1865, Assistant Surgeon George M. McGill, U.S.A., amputated the limb at the knee joint by making a long anterior and short posterior flap and retaining the patella. The stump healed favorably. Four months after the injury, the patella having greatly retracted, was drawn over the supracondyloid space and fixed by a bandage. On November 22, 1865, Corporal Cole was discharged from service and sent to New York to have an artificial limb by Dr. E.D. Hudson. The broad condyles offered an admirable base of support. The cicatrix was firm. The limb answered an excellent purpose. In 1868, Cole was living at his home in Spring Valley, New York, and walked without a cane. In March, 1874, he was still a pensioner.

Photographed at the Army Medical Museum.

By order of the Surgeon General:

GEORGE A. OTIS
Assistant Surgeon, U.S.A., Curator, A.M.M.

XV.
Hip

Injuries to the hip were considered the gravest of all gunshot wounds because of high mortality rates despite various treatments methods [see Table 12]. Hamilton was a proponent of conservative measures because "gunshot fractures of the head and neck of the femur almost always terminate fatally under amputation or excision, and equally under treatment as fractures, that is, where an attempt is made to save the limb without interference with the knife."[17] Conservative treatment revolved around different means to provide traction. The familiar Buck's traction apparatus, frequently employed preoperatively for hip fractures today, was developed and used during the Civil War. Surgeons who decided upon conservative management of these fractures, were recommended to use "...Buck's apparatus, with moderate extension (five to ten pounds). Hodgen's straight splint, or 'cradle' has been found exceedingly useful, and much preferable to any form of double inclined plane..."[17] One medical manual even advised using fifteen to thirty pounds when using Buck's traction.[24]

Smith's anterior splint was also commonly used. Many other types of lower extremity fractures were treated by surgeons on both sides using Smith's wire splint. One grateful physician referred to it as "a blessing to the Confederate surgeons...It is so simple, so easily and quickly made, so cheap, and so easily adapted to almost every fracture that it was generally used."[1] Smith's anterior splint was not well received early on by many physicians because of poor results from incorrect application of the splint. Improper application led to malunions and ulcerations, and medical journals had to carry descriptions of proper application of the splint to prevent further iatrogenic injuries.[35] Suspension was from the ceiling, and traction of the limb was provided by moving the bed back from the ceiling attachment. Surgeons were advised to increase the suspension further out from the body for proximal fractures of lower extremity. For distal fractures (i.e., ankle region), the suspension was almost straight up vertically. Blocks under the foot of the bed could be used to give additional counter traction and prevent the soldier

Buck's traction.

Hodgen's splint.

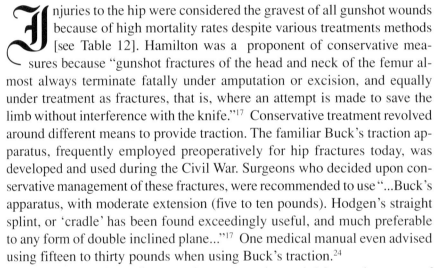

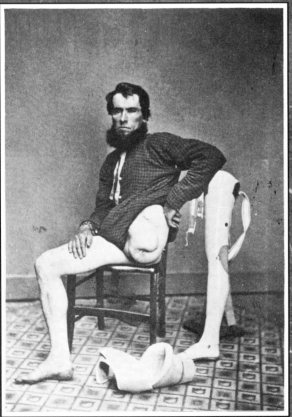

Surgeon General's Office
ARMY MEDICAL MUSEUM

Photograph No. 196 and 197. *Case of successful primary amputation at the hip-joint.*

Private James E. Kelley, B., 56th Pennsylvania, age twenty-eight, was wounded at about 9:00 in the morning of April 29, 1863, in a skirmish of the 1st Division, 1st Corps, on the Rappahannock, nearly opposite the "Pratte House" below Fredericksburg. A conoidal musket ball fired from a distance of about three hundred yards shattered his left femur. A consultation of the senior surgeons of the brigades decided that ex-articulation of the femur was expedient and the operation was performed at 4:00 in the afternoon at the "Fitzhugh House" by surgeon Edward Shippen, U.S.V., and the amputation was accomplished with slight loss of blood. The patient was, at first, placed in a hospital tent, was transferred May 22 to the Corps Hospital, progressing favorably. By May 28 all the ligatures had been removed. On June 15, 1863, the patient was captured by the enemy and removed to the Libby Prison in Richmond. Up to this date there had been no adverse symptoms. On July 14, Kelley was exchanged and sent to the Annapolis, U.S.A., General Hospital. On his admission he was much exhausted by profuse diarrhea. The internal portion of the wound had united but the external portion was gangrenous. Applications of bromine were made to the sloughing surface without amelioration. A chlorinated soda solution was substituted, and in the latter part of July there was a healthy granulating surface. On December 23, 1863, the wound had entirely healed and Kelley visited Washington and obtained an honorable discharge from service and a pension. At this date, the picture from which the photograph was taken was drawn by Hospital Steward Stauch, U.S.A., one of the artists of the Army Medical Museum. Kelley then went to his home, near Black Lake P.O., Indiana County, Pennsylvania. A letter dated January 12, 1865, was received from him at this office and represented him as in excellent health and spirits at the time. In the spring of 1868, Kelley went to New York and had an artificial limb adapted by Dr. E.D. Hudson. At that time the photograph was taken. He could walk quite well after the adaptation of the artificial limb. This specimen is preserved at the Army Medical Museum and is number 1148 of the surgical section. Kelley's disability was rated March 4, 1874, as total, second grade. There was nothing additional recorded at the pension office at the above date.

Photographed at the Army Medical Museum.

By order of the Surgeon General:

GEORGE A. OTIS
Assistant Surgeon, U.S.A., Curator, A.M.M.

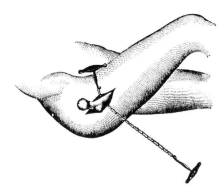

A hip resection is shown being performed through a longitudinal incision with a chain saw.

from being pulled off the bed. Regardless of the traction used, morbidity was fairly significant, with the injured limb healing with shortening, deformity and ankylosis. Despite the formidable morbidity with hip fractures, there were a number of case reports of soldiers ambulating without use of crutches.

Other surgeons felt excision of the hip provided the best chances at survival. George A. Otis, one of the chief editors for the *Medical and Surgical History of the War of the Rebellion,* advocated: "When the injury is principally confined to the bone, and the question arises whether to let the patient alone, to amputate at the hip, or to excise the joint, I should not hesitate in preferring the last resource." The surgical approach was usually through a lateral longitudinal incision centered over the greater trochanter, and best results were obtained when surgery was done early. Of a total of sixty-six documented excisions, there were six who survived. Fifteen of the excisions were performed by Confederate surgeons.[20] All cases that had extensive involvement of the acetabulum terminated fatally. Postoperative treatment included rest and longitudinal traction by Buck's traction or a hanging sling to position the femur at 20° from horizontal.[16] The survivors of this operation were generally able to bear a considerable amount of weight with the addition of a cane and shoe lift.[2]

Hip disarticulation was perhaps the largest and most difficult procedure performed during the war. Twenty of the sixty-six hip amputations attempted were done by Confederate surgeons. The usual incisions adopted for this procedure formed an anterior and posterior flap. Occasionally a single flap or circular closure was performed. Reports of blood loss were minimal due to skilled ligature of vessels and the occasional use of an "abdominal tourniquet," which compressed the aorta. The feeling by the end of the war was that the procedure was justified—especially secondarily—but not without a tremendous functional and cosmetic sacrifice.[36] Intermediate staged amputations, after the beginning of inflammation, had 100% mortality. Secondary stage operations did the best with a mortality rate of 77.8%.[2] The excessive mortality of this procedure caused one Confederate surgeon to remark that to perform a hip disarticulation was "an unfortunate ambition—we might even use a stronger term for it—a criminal desire, to have an amputation at the hip-joint in the list of operations performed, which misleads many surgeons to perform this disarticulation, when their better judgment teaches them that it must be a useless mutilation."[37] Several records of the survivors of this procedure, with follow-up as long as four years after the surgery, indicated relatively good health and the ability to use crutches for mobility, but a widespread nonacceptance of any prostheses secondary to stump irritation, poor function, and patient fatigue.[2]

𝕮𝖆𝖇𝖑𝖊 12.
𝕽𝖊𝖘𝖚𝖑𝖙𝖘 𝖔𝖋
𝕿𝖗𝖊𝖆𝖙𝖒𝖊𝖓𝖙𝖘 𝖔𝖋
𝕲𝖚𝖓𝖘𝖍𝖔𝖙 𝖂𝖔𝖚𝖓𝖉𝖘 𝖙𝖔
𝖙𝖍𝖊 𝕳𝖎𝖕 [2]

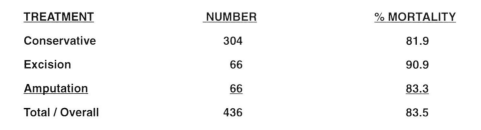

TREATMENT	NUMBER	% MORTALITY
Conservative	304	81.9
Excision	66	90.9
Amputation	66	83.3
Total / Overall	436	83.5

XVI.

Thigh

Almost 10,000 gunshot wounds of the femur were recorded during the course of the war [see Table 13]. Surgeons classified the results of treatment not only by stage but also by location. The mortality rate increased in proportion to a more proximal wound location: as the level of amputation moved up the leg, so did the chance of death. Conservative management consisted of either Buck's traction, Smith's anterior wire splint, Hodgen's splint, or other forms of traction. Hodgen's suspension cradle splint became the forerunner of the well-known Thomas splint made famous in World War I. This mode of treatment commonly led to limbs that healed, but not without shortening of the limb averaging almost two inches, and occasional angulation. Additional morbidity resulted from stiff knee joints. The average recovery period for a survivor was 104 days.[38] Transportation of soldiers with proximal lower extremity fractures could be accomplished in specially outfitted ambulances, although the availability of these were variable.[24]

Excision in the shaft of the femur usually resulted in a great amount of shortening. Thus, the functional outcomes showed considerable variability in the ability to ambulate with a prosthesis following this procedure. Excision procedures were thought of as unfavorable by both sides, both concerning survival and utility of the leg.

The majority of amputations done in the thigh area were done for shot fractures at the knee or below. Those who had amputations for gunshot fractures of the femur had a mortality rate of just over 50% in either Union or Confederate surgeons' hands. There were twenty recorded cases of bilateral thigh amputations. One of these survivors with bilateral prostheses "could walk with ease on level ground, get up and down stairs readily." In addition, the man worked as a clerk at the U.S. Treasury following the war.[2] Another example, Lieutenant General John B. Hood, survived a proximal thigh amputation following a gunshot fracture of the femur during the Battle of Chickamauga. After he recovered, he continued to serve, commanding from

As the level of amputation moved up the leg, so did the chance of death.

horseback while strapped into the saddle.[32]

When reviewing lower extremity trauma, one important caveat learned from the war was that conservative treatment, when applicable, provided the best results. This view differed from opinions formed in previous wars, including the Napoleonic and Crimean wars. Amputation was to be resorted to only when extensive comminution, soft tissue loss, or neurovascular injury existed. This changing attitude was summed up by one Union surgeon who addressed the College of Physicians and Surgeons in New York: "I have observed that good military surgeons pass, as it were, through three stages in their judgment of gunshot fractures of the thigh: the first is that they do not regard these injuries as so dangerous as they really are...After the surgeon has had an opportunity of witnessing this result in the majority of cases, he hopes for better results from primary amputation...after bitter experience has shown that thigh amputations for gunshot fractures are in themselves so dangerous that but few survive, he then settles down into a good, prudent, and conservative surgeon ...who will never operate for the sake of operating."[39]

On the Confederate side, there were more arguments to support the cause of amputation: the ability to transport the injured soldier more easily, increased comfort during transport, and less hospital recovery time required.[29] Not only did Confederate military strategy demand greater mobility since they were generally outnumbered, forcing the need for quick movements to reinforce defensive lines, they also recorded slightly better survival rates with amputation than conservative treatment. Both sides did agree upon conservative treatment, if at all possible, for gunshot fractures of the upper thigh because the results of amputation in this area were frightfully poor.

During the war, an article appeared in the *Confederate States Medical and Surgical Journal* proposing the use of an external fixator. The procedure had been performed on a laborer in 1853 who had a nonunion of the femur. The fixator had one "pin" in each bone and rotation around the pins was controlled with external splints. An editor's note cautioned: "It may be objected that by this method a simple fracture may be converted into a compound one; but....In the case of a gunshot wound the fracture is compound already."[7] There is no recorded use of this device during the war. There was also one case of an attempted open reduction and internal fixation of femur utilizing silver wire. The patient, however, died three days after the procedure following transportation to another hospital.[2]

𝔗able 13. 𝔑esults of 𝔗reatments of 𝔊unshot 𝔚ounds to the 𝔉emur, 𝔑ot 𝔍nvolving the 𝔍oints [2]

TREATMENT	NUMBER	% MORTALITY
Conservative	3476	49.9
Excision	175	69.4
Amputation	6229	53.8
Total / Overall	9880	52.7

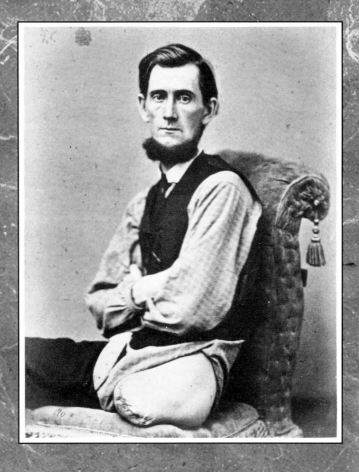

Surgeon General's Office

ARMY MEDICAL MUSEUM

Photograph No. 190. *Stump of left thigh amputated primarily for gunshot fracture.*

Private John N. Taggert, G, 1st Virginia Light Artillery, had the shaft of his left femur shattered by a fragment of shell at Rocky Gap, August 26, 1863. Surgeon Wynne, 14th Pennsylvania Cavalry, amputated the limb at the junction of the upper third of the femur on the same day, by antero-posterior flaps. The wound healed very rapidly. He was sent to a hospital at Pittsburgh. In less than a month the stump was firmly healed. In April, 1864, he was transferred to the Christian Street Hospital, Philadelphia, and was thence discharged form service on June 14, 1864. On November 12, 1867, Mr. Taggert visited the Army Medical Museum in excellent health and his stump was photographed. He died of consumption, October 26, 1870.

Photographed at the Army Medical Museum.

By order of the Surgeon General:

GEORGE A. OTIS
Assistant Surgeon, U.S.A., Curator, A.M.M.

XVII.

Knee

Due to the dismal mortality rate of gunshot fractures to the knee joint, most surgeons argued for thigh amputations.

Similar to injuries of other joints, gunshot fractures that involved the knee joint had a disproportionately high mortality rate when compared to wounds occurring in adjacent areas. Conservative treatment yielded a mortality rate of 60.6%.[2] Because of this dismal mortality rate, most surgeons argued for thigh amputations to be performed. A proponent of conservative treatment, Dr. Joseph Jones wrote: "In knee joint injuries, which, when not operated on, have heretofore been considered as almost fatal, nearly fifty percent were cured by securing rest, immobility of the injured joint and by employing the cold water dressing (irrigation being preferred) and by the free use of opium."[1] Conservative treatment of patella fractures involved applying strips of adhesive plaster above and below the fracture site and a splint behind the knee to prevent flexion.[24]

Excision of the knee was frowned upon because of poor results. The one exception to this was if the injury and resection involved only the patella. For a full knee excision, surgeons were advised to use iron or silver sutures to bring the femur and tibia into opposition with each other. There are no records however that recorded this procedure ever being done. A well- padded posterior splint was usually applied and a successful result was one in which there was complete bony ankylosis or fusion.[16] Only eight of the fifty-seven knee excision cases actually survived the operation. One survivor, Captain C. Knowlton, had a pension examiner write that he walked well and could "dance even, round dances." He did, however, develop a complete ankylosis of the joint.[2]

The average knee amputation took two to three minutes. Overall mortality from the procedure was 51.1%.[2] Because of the mortality rate of knee disarticulation, the vast majority (2,377 of 3,355) were treated by thigh amputations. Hamilton postulated, based upon experiences from the war, that amputation was the only recourse "when the fracture implicates the knee joint, or even when it is near the knee joint, experience having shown that amputations near the knee joint give a better percentage of recoveries than

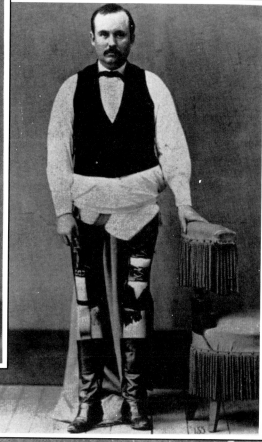

Surgeon General's Office

ARMY MEDICAL MUSEUM

Photographs 154 and 155. *Successful double amputation right thigh and left leg.*

On July 8, 1863 Private Charles N. Lapham, Company K, 1st Vermont Cavalry, aged 23 years, in a skirmish in Boonesborough, Maryland was struck by a solid shot which carried away both legs. The shock was of course excessive; but he rallied and forty-eight hours afterwards he was placed under the influence of chloroform and the right limb in which the knee joint was gravely injured, was amputated at mid thigh while the left was disarticulated at the knee. Antero-posterior flap operations were done in both instances. He recovered with extraordinary rapidity in as much as on August 25, six weeks after the reception of the injury, the stumps were firmly cicatrized and he was discharged from service. Eleven months afterward he was supplied with artificial limbs by Dr. E.D. Hudson. In October, 1864, he wrote from Poughkeepsie Collegiate Institute where he was studying, that he could walk well on level ground and ascend and descend a staircase readily; and he contributed the photographs from which these are enlarged. In March 1874, Mr. Lapham was employed in the second auditor's office, Treasury Department.

Photographed at the Army Medical Museum.

By order of the Surgeon General:

GEORGE A. OTIS
Ass't Surgeon, U.S.A., Curator, A.M.M.

any other thigh amputation, while, on the other hand, attempts to save the limb in these cases give a worse percentage of success than in any other fractures of the thigh."[31] Confederate Major General R.S. Ewell was an example of this philosophy. He was injured at Second Manassas, sustaining a gunshot fracture of the patella and knee joint. He underwent a thigh amputation. Postoperatively, he endured a fifty-mile stretcher ride to avoid capture by the enemy, and he eventually went on to serve in the field again.[2]

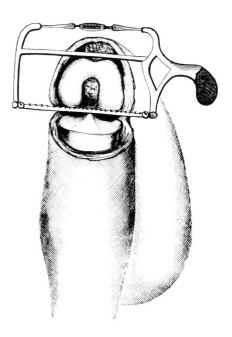

The articular surfaces of the joint are being resected by a back-cutting saw during a knee resection.

A sidebar:

Your Day in the Operating Room

Civil War operations violated almost every method of infection prevention we use to day. The medical corp was poorly organized, particularly at the beginning of the war. There were huge numbers of casualties that no one was prepared to handle. It was not uncommon for a wounded soldier to remain on the battlefield for forty-eight hours or more prior to receiving definitive care.

Following an injury, a wounded soldier was moved close to a field hospital. There he often waited on the ground or a pile of straw. An operating brigade would then evaluate the injured and triage each soldier to determine the severity of the injury and decide who would be treated first. "Dressing surgeons" then treated the less seriously injured.

Operating tables were often doors taken off their hinges. Many of the surgeries were performed outside or in the light of large windows.

The soldier was then placed on the table and administered the anesthetic, most often chloroform. Once he was asleep, the anesthetic was removed from his face. The wound was then probed with a finger or blunt instrument. The surgeon's hands were rarely clean and often could not be washed for hours or days at a time. Open wounds were then treated by placement of lint or cotton and kept wet, "sweet and clean." If an amputation or surgical procedure was planned, it was usually performed immediately prior to the "irrative stage" of inflammation and infection. Occasionally, the patient in shock was allowed to "rally" prior to the operation, although without the benefit of intravenous fluid this was rarely beneficial.

"We operated in old blood-stained and pus stained coats, the veterans of a hundred fights . . . We used undisinfected hands and undisinfected instruments, and still worse used marine sponges which had been used in prior pus cases . . ."

XVIII.
Leg

*Survivors often had
lifelong draining wounds.*

Gunshot fractures of the leg constituted the most common fractures of the long bones. Conservative treatment included fracture boxes, Smith's anterior splints, Hodgen's cradle splint, and other splints. Overall mortality for conservative treatment was 13.8%.[2] Frequently, survivors had lifelong draining wounds.

Excisions in this area had poor results in terms of morbidity and mortality. Overall mortality for excisions in this area was 28.2% (61.1% if both bones were excised).[2] Excisions as a whole resulted in Achilles tendon contractions and poor weight-bearing ability. The only cases that had acceptable functional results were the few that involved excision of the midshaft area of the fibula only. One Union surgeon, referring to a case of a ten-inch tibial excision, commented that "no more useless or unphilosophical operation could be devised than the one done in this case."[2] The majority of injuries in this area were treated by amputation just below the knee or by thigh amputation. One of the more noted cases of a thigh amputation for a distal fracture was Major General Dan E. Sickles at Gettysburg. He sustained a shattered tibia-fibula fracture when he was struck by a cannonball. Sickles was carried off the field smoking a cigar in order to masquerade the seriousness of his injury to his men. He had his leg amputated at the distal thigh on the field. He recovered and donated his amputated limb to the Army Medical Museum. He was known to visit his donated limb after the war on several occasions.

Secondary amputations, performed over thirty days after the original injury, had the lowest mortality rate. The general amputation guidelines for this area were: "Gunshot fractures of the shafts of both the tibia and fibula demand amputation where the comminution is extensive, or the pulsation of the posterior tibial artery is lost, or the foot is cold and insensible."[17]

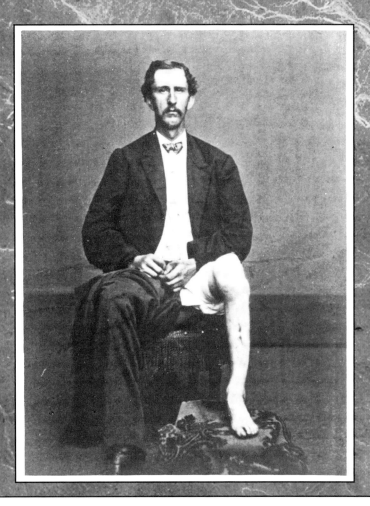

Surgeon General's Office
ARMY MEDICAL MUSEUM

Photograph No. 237. *Successful excision of left tibia.*

Lieutenant O.R. Tyler, Battery I, 2nd Connecticut Heavy Artillery, was wounded at Opequan Creek near Winchester, Virginia on September 19, 1864, by a conoidal musket ball, which fractured and comminuted the left tibia in the middle third. On the same day he was sent to the depot Field Hospital where Surgeon Henry Plumb, 2nd Connecticut Heavy Artillery, by a linear incision along the inner anterior aspect, excised three inches of the bone which was much comminuted. Patient's general condition was satisfactory; simple dressings were applied. On November 12 he was transferred to the hospital in Frederick, Maryland, whereon December 15th the missile and fragments of bone were removed. By January 13, 1865, when he was furloughed there had been no bony deposit in the inner space. He was discharged from service March 9, 1865. In June, 1865, Dr. E.D. Hudson, who furnished a patient an apparatus for supporting the limb, reported that there was no shortening of the limb, but that it was considerably atrophied with lateral excurvature; the head of the fibula was partially detached by reluxation of the ligaments and the flexor muscles of the foot were impaired. A thin osseous tissue not continuous or united, supplied the place of the missing bone but afforded no support.

Photographed at the Army Medical Museum.

By order of the Surgeon General:

GEORGE A. OTIS
Ass't Surg., U.S.A., Curator, A.M.M.

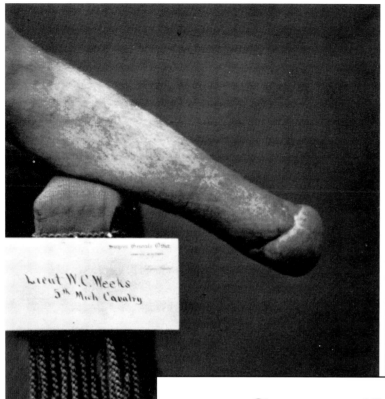

Lieut W.C. Weeks
5ᵗʰ Mich Cavalry

𝕾𝖚𝖗𝖌𝖊𝖔𝖓 𝕲𝖊𝖓𝖊𝖗𝖆𝖑'𝖘 𝕺𝖋𝖋𝖎𝖈𝖊

ARMY MEDICAL MUSEUM

Photograph No. 75. *Successful amputation of the left ankle by a method of Pirogoff.*

Lieutenant W.C. Weeks, I, 5th Michigan Cavalry, was wounded April 1, 1865, at the Battle of Five Forks by a conoidal musket ball which passed through his left ankle joint. He was immediately carried to the hospital at City Point and amputation at the ankle joint was performed on the same day by Surgeon A.K. St. Clair, 5th Michigan Cavalry. The articulating surface of the tibia and calcaneum were removed and the cut surfaces were brought into opposition. On April 16, 1865, the patient was transferred to Armory Square Hospital at Washington. On admission he was in a feeble condition. An erysipelatous blush extended above the knee on the injured side; an abscess had formed in the lower part of the leg and no union of the flap had taken place. With the employment of stimulants and nutrition with emollient applications to the limb, there was a gradual improvement until April 28, 1865, when symptoms of pyemic infection supervened. Rapidly recurring chills, icteroid colorization of the skin and conjunctiva, anorexia, and a frequent feeble pulse suggested the gravest prognosis. Energetic treatment was adopted. An ounce of brandy was given every two hours, and quinine, sesquichloroid and beef tea were freely administered. On May 6, the grave symptoms began to subside, and by the end of the month, the patient was fairly convalescent. On June 26, the patient was pronounced well. The osseous calcaneus had firmly united to the tibia and there was a good solid stump. A cast in plaster was taken of it (A.M.M. Spec. 2298). In a few days subsequently, a photograph was taken. Mr. Weeks was wearing the Palmar limb with satisfaction in December, 1873.

Photographed at the Army Medical Museum.

By order of the Surgeon General:

GEORGE A. OTIS
Assistant Surgeon, U.S.A., Curator, A.M.M.

XIX.
Ankle

Most fractures in this area were treated with proximal amputation, usually below the knee. Surgeons had the same apprehension of wounds to the ankle as they did of the knee, so fewer than one-third of gunshot fractures of the ankle were treated conservatively. They discovered that late disabilities ensued with conservative measures. Ankle amputation methods included both Pirogoff's and Syme's methods. Syme's method was the most common. There was a slightly higher mortality rate for amputations using Pirogoff's method, but amputations that employed Syme's methods had a higher reamputation rate.

The debate over which surgery gave better results continued throughout the war. Both surgeries retained the heel pad to surface the end of the amputation stump. However, the Syme amputation removes all the bones of the foot, retaining the heel pad to be sewn to the end of the tibia. Pirogoff's method retains the calcaneous and attempts to unite the calcaneous to the end of the tibia. The advantage of Pirogoff's method was that the length of the limb was maintained, making it easier to bear weight on the end of the stump. The disadvantage was that there was little or no room to place an artificial ankle joint for an ankle or foot prosthesis. Also, with Pirogoff's method the healing of the calcaneous to the tibia was not always predictable.

Excision of ankle was rarely done. If the talus or major ankle bone was not reducible, compound, or dislocated, talectomy was advised.[16]

The debate over whether Pirogoff's or Syme's method was better raged throughout the war.

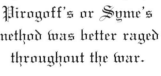

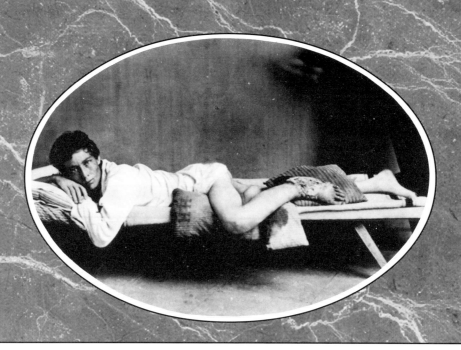

𝕾urgeon 𝕲eneral's 𝕺ffice

ARMY MEDICAL MUSEUM

Ulcer on foot. Gangrene. Amputation. Recovery.

John D. Parmenter, private, Co. G., 67th Pa. Vols., was admitted to Harewood U.S.A. Hospital April 16th, 1865, suffering from a gangrenous ulcer on the external side of the left foot over malleolus, result of a gunshot wound received at the battle of Amelia Springs, Va., April 6th, 1865. Amputation of left leg, lower third, by a circular incision June 21st, 1865.

Photographed at the Army Medical Museum.

By order of the Surgeon General:

GEORGE A. OTIS
Assistant Surgeon, U.S.A., Curator, A.M.M.

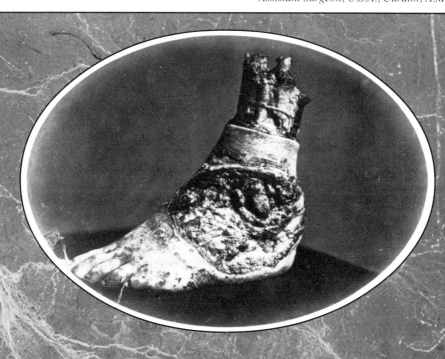

XX.
Foot

Fractures of the tarsal and metatarsals were treated predominantly conservatively in anterior to posterior pasteboard splints or in a fracture box if the soldier was being transported.[24] Overall mortality for gunshot fractures of the foot was 8.3%. The surgeons discovered calcaneus fractures healed well without operative interference. When amputation was resorted to in the mid-foot, Chopart's and Lisfranc's levels of amputation were utilized and reported in over 100 cases. There was an emphasis on minimizing areas to be debrided similar to the philosophy of hand wounds. Surgeons realized after the war that conservative treatment had led to an unacceptable amount of useless limbs because of injuries to the foot when compared to functional results of those fitted with prostheses.[2]

Chopart's and Lisfranc's levels of amputation were used when amputatoin was resorted to.

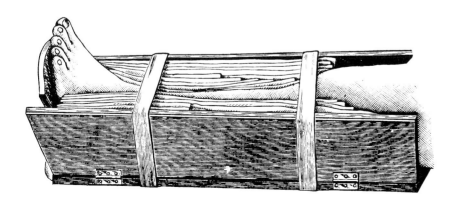

A fracture box was often used if the wounded soldier needed to be transported.

XXI.
Nerbe Injuries

Causalgia was
—and is—
difficult to treat.

Studies were undertaken during the war to detail the effect of gunshot wounds upon peripheral nerves. These studies detailed that motor function was more severely affected than sensory function. The first descriptions of what is known today as causalgia or refex sympathetic dystrophy were published during the war. Physicians who observed the phenomenon in certain gunshot wounds of the upper extremity described the fingers, which were: "Affected as usually tapering, smooth, hairless, almost void of wrinkles, glossy, pink or ruddy, or blotched...very painful, especially on motion, and pain often extending from the hand up the arm." Nineteen cases were reported and the pain was described as "a case of the most terrible suffering, from a combination of burning pain in the hand and neuralgic pain in the forearm."[40] Surgeons noted that causalgia was from partial rather than complete nerve wounds and that it could affect surrounding joints. Causalgia was found to be very difficult to treat—as it still is today. The first major treatise on this subject was written in 1864: *Gunshot Wounds and Other Injuries of Nerves* by Mitchell, Morehouse, and Keen.[40] It was based on their careful observation of hundreds of Civil War soldiers with nerve injuries.

Nerve suturing was also advocated for torn peripheral nerves.[22] This was a major advancement since at the beginning of the war there was a widely held myth that manipulation of a large nerve could cause a heart attack or death.

XXII.
Prosthetics

The large number of amputations and resections performed during the war drew attention to the need for a large supply of prosthetics and specially trained people designing prosthetics for specific injuries. In 1866 the state of Mississippi alone spent one-fifth of the state's revenue on artificial limbs.[1] The Association for the Relief of Maimed Soldiers placed in their organization's constitution this provision: "To supply artificial limbs for all officers, soldiers and seamen who have been maimed in the service of their country..." This organization spent $125,000 to outfit 769 soldiers who had undergone amputations with prostheses.[1]

Even before the war ended, the demand for artificial limbs was evident. Early in the war, one Southern doctor wrote: "It is creditable to the ingenuity of our people to say that, in spite of many difficulties, it is probable that a sufficient number of good and serviceable legs can be manufactured in the Confederacy."[41] However, by 1864 it was thought that only one-tenth of the demand for limbs could be supplied in the Confederacy.[42] Surgeons were advised that amputations should be performed at the junction of the middle and distal thirds of the tibia, "then from this point the surgeon should not recede unless compelled by necessity. He should contest every inch until driven to the knee joint. But he should never operate through the knee joint, as nothing is gained by it while much is lost, because the end of the

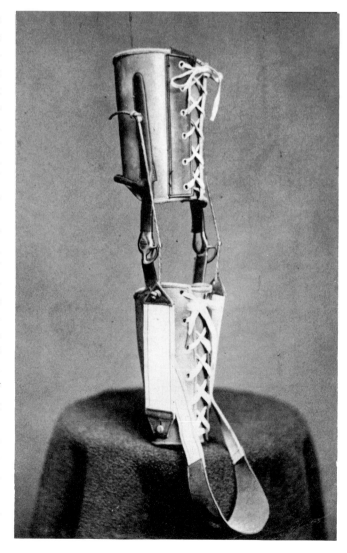

The large-scale damage done to limbs during the Civil War created the need for plentiful and innovative prosthetics.

femur will occupy space which is needed for the construction of an artificial knee joint." The anterior-posterior flap amputation method was recommended for the use in a prosthesis because other flaps were felt to cause pressure points.[43]

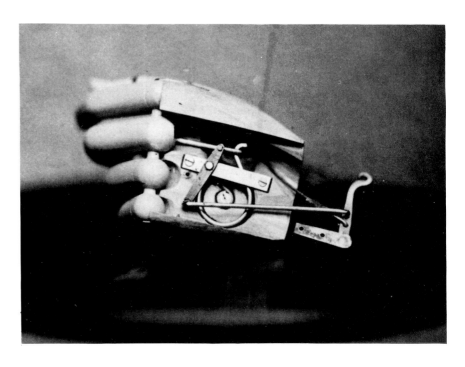

Upper extremity prosthetics were difficult to engineer secondary to the complex functions required. Shown is an early attempt at an innovative hand prosthetic.

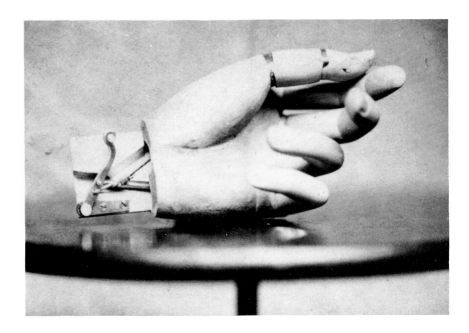

Surgeon General's Office

ARMY MEDICAL MUSEUM

Photograph No. 107. *Successful excision of the upper portion of the shaft of the right femur.*

At the Battle of Cold Harbor, June 3, 1864, Private Jason W. Joslyn, Company I, 7th New York Heavy Artillery, aged 21 years, was struck in the right gluteal region by a conoidal musket ball, which passed forwards and downwards striking the femur a little below the trochanter major, and comminuting the upper third of the shaft. He fell into the hands of the enemy and on June 5, fifty-four hours after the reception of the injury an excision of the shattered femur was made through a vertical linear incision commencing near the upper point of the trochanter major and carried downwards seven and a half inches, in the axis of the limb. The femur was divided between the trochanters by a chain saw and again, six and a half inches below. The operation was performed at a field hospital by a Confederate surgeon. On the same day the patient was placed in an ambulance and sent to Richmond, a distance of thirteen miles, and placed in Hospital #21 in charge of Surgeon G.W. Semple. He states that he was very weak and exhausted upon arriving at the hospital. His limb was placed in a fracture box, and he was ordered two ounces of whiskey twice daily and a diet of corn and wheat bread with salt. Towards the end of June there was extensive sloughing of the soft parts on the outer sides of the thigh. Joslyn remained in the hospital in Richmond until August 22, 1864 when he was paroled and sent into the Union lines. He was conveyed on the steamer New York to the general hospital at Annapolis....Assistant surgeon D.C. Peters, US Army in charge of Jarvis Hospital [where he was subsequently sent], reported that as a result of his examination that in consequence in fracture of the neck and great trochanter by a fragment of shell, the head and about two inches of the shaft had been removed; that the limb was shortened six inches and could be swung backwards and forwards but not rotated or abducted. Surgeon Cyrus N. Chamberlain...found that the upper extremity of the femur was much enlarged, and that a good false joint had formed....But while that report was in press, evidence was adduced that the excision did not involve an ex-articulation. It was too late to withdraw the case from tables; but a memorandum was inserted that the report might not mislead. On August 29, 1865, Joslyn was transferred to De Camp Hospital, David's Island, New York. Here a critical examination of the limb was made by Assistant Surgeon Warren Webster, U.S. Army, and Professor F.H. Hamilton. There can be no doubt that the head of the femur still occupied the acetabulum. There was a great deposit of new bone at the reunion of the trochanter major and the upper extremity of the resected shaft. The shortening was six and a half inches by careful measurement. Joslyn could bear his entire weight on the limb. The thigh could be flexed and extended naturally. When it was rotated the trochanter major could be felt going through its circuit. The thigh and leg were atrophied; the cicatrix was extensive, owing probably to the sloughing that took place soon after the operation, but it was firm and healthy; the gastrocnemius and the extensors of the foot were rigid; the foot was extended to the utmost. In October, 1865, Dr. E.D. Hudson supplied the patient with an ingenious prosthetic apparatus, consisting of a case of rawhides, laced upon the thigh and leg and terminating in an artificial foot with ginglymoid articulations at the ankle and toes. With this apparatus, Joslyn could walk with ease, aided by a light cane.

Photographed at the Army Medical Museum.

By order of the Surgeon General:

GEORGE A. OTIS
Bv't Lt. Col., Ass't Surg., U.S.A., Curator, A.M.M.

XXIII.
Conclusion

"Already, nearly ten thousand maimed men in the Confederate States carry with them stumps . . . "

Shortly after the war, medical records were compiled and published by the Surgeon General's office, creating a truly remarkable series: *Medical and Surgical History of the War of the Rebellion.* As mentioned previously, this set is an invaluable source of data, case histories, and photographs regarding medical treatment during the conflict. It was one of the first achievements of American academic medicine recognized in Europe. Other accomplishments included mass casualty management systems, the origin of nursing in the United States, and, at the completion of the war, the importance of sanitation and hygiene. The Army Medical Museum, which eventually became the Armed Forces Institute of Pathology, was formed during the Civil War. The number of surgeons with practical experience in the management of trauma and military surgery greatly expanded, leading to the eventual formation of societies of specialization that occurred during the remainder of the nineteenth century. One direct example of this was the formation of a maxillofacial surgery hospital in the south directed by James B. Bean.

One writer anticipated the development of orthopaedics as a specialty when he wrote: "Already, nearly ten thousand maimed men in the Confederate States carry with them stumps which will be examined soon by those specialists, who are experts in this limited field of anatomy and mechanical philosophy."[42] The Civil War intensified study of the treatment of bone infections such as osteomyelitis. The formation of the first orthopaedic professorship in 1861 by Lewis A. Sayre and the first substantial orthopaedic residency in 1863 under James Knight were both started during the war. After the war, several orthopaedic hospitals opened under the directorship of surgeons trained during the war.[22] The American Civil War provided both the caseload and the surgical training to hasten the recognition of orthopaedics as a distinct specialty. The first major hospital to recognize orthopaedics as a specialty did so in 1872, and the first U.S. orthopaedic organization was the American Orthopaedic Association, formed in 1887, twenty-two years after the war ended. A review of the history of surgical treatment administered over 130 years ago during the Civil War is in actuality a basis for orthopaedic procedures practiced today.

Orthopaedic and extremity trauma management has progressed considerably since the Civil War. However, a number of basic principles used during the war remain in practice even today. Open, contaminated fractures are meticulously debrided, cleaned, and closed in a delayed fashion in today's modern trauma centers. Antibiotics and aseptic technique have helped tremendously in lowering infection rates. The invention of the *x*-ray has allowed accurate diagnosis of fracture types. Splinting and traction are still utilized, but current orthopaedic surgeons also use screws, plates, wires, rods, external fixators, artifical joints, and a whole host of other techniques for treating fractures. Many previously untreatable neurovascular injuries can now be repaired using microscopes, meticulous suturing techniques, and suture material finer than a human hair. Handling of tissues with special instruments is used to avoid further tissue injury. Today's plastic surgeons, using microsurgical techniques, can now take healthy tissue from another part of the body and use it to reconstruct or cover large areas of skin, muscle, and bone loss. Specialty nursing care and physical tharapy can help to achieve good functional results, even after severe extremity trauma.

Roughly 50,000 total amputations were performed by both sides during the Civil War. This is compared to just over 4,000 amputations performed on four million American soldiers in World War I and nearly 16,000 amputations performed on eleven million Americans engaged in World War II. This drop in the amputation rate was in spite of an increase and advancement in weaponry, and was due to improved wound care methods and speedy evacuation of soldiers from the battlefield. Most amputations are done today because of diseases such as diabetes or hardening of the arteries. Amputation may still be required for mangled extremities from severe automobile or farm accidents, gunshot wounds, or other forms of trauma. The modern surgeon continues to follow the edict proposed during the Civil War by Samuel D. Gross, M.D.: ". . . the surgeon endeavors to avoid . . . mutilating a limb that might have been saved, and endangering life by the retention of one that should have been promptly amputated." Fortunately, secondary to the advancement of medical science, the incidence of having to resort to amputation is much more infrequent.

Just as in other specialties, the incredible volume of human trauma sustained by soldiers during this time period provided knowledge and experience to surgeons of the time—experience at a high price, experience for which we can be very grateful. Although this historical background and evaluation of the types of treatments provided may seem naïve in hindsight, as one Confederate medical officer wrote years after the war, "We did not do the best we would, but the best we could."

Civil War surgical treatments are in actuality a basis for today's orthopaedic practices.

XXIV.
Glossary

abduction	movement of an extremity away from the midline of the body.
acetabulum	the portion of the pelvic bones that forms the socket of the hip joint.
acromion	the most lateral bony projection of the tip of the shoulder.
ankylosis (anchylosis)	when a joint has become immobile or frozen secondary to scarring or other trauma.
anterior	referring to anatomy that is in the front.
antiseptic	an agent (usually chemical) that prevents or inhibits bacterial growth.
articulation	a joint.
atrophy	shrinkage secondary to injury or activity.
axilla	the armpit.
Buck's traction	a type of traction applied to the leg where the force is applied in line with the leg; named after Gurdon Buck, 1807-77.
calcaneus	the heelbone
causalgia	a severe, unremitting burning pain usually due to injury of a nerve.
cellulitis	inflammation that spreads through the skin planes, usually from an infection.
cervical	pertaining to the region of the neck.
Chopart's amputation	a level of amputation through the mid-portion of the foot, named after Francois Chopart, 1743-95.
clavicle	the collarbone.
coccyx	the tailbone.

communited	referring to a fracture where the bone is splintered or in many pieces.
conservative	nonsurgical treatment.
coracoid	a portion of the scapula projecting anteriorly.
Dakin's solution	an antiseptic made with dilute sodium hypochlorite used extensively in World War I; named after Henry Dakin, 1880-1952.
debridement	the act of removing foreign material and dead tissue from a wound.
deltoid	the muscle covering the shoulder prominence.
disarticulation	to separate a joint, usually by amputation.
distal	an anatomical location more distant from the head.
erysipelas	a severe infection caused by Streptococcus, having skin manifestations.
excision	to remove only a portion of a bone.
expectant	nonoperative; see *conservative*.
external fixator	an apparatus designed to stabilize a fracture with an external frame attached to pins that are in the bone above and below the fracture site.
femur	the thigh bone. The head of the femur is the ball of the hip joint. The greater, or major, trochanter is the palpable lateral prominence over the hip joint.
fibula	the outer bone of the leg.
fistula	an abnormal connection between a body cavity and the surface or another cavity.
foramen	an opening in the bone that allows passage of nerve or vessels.
functional position	a position of the joint which is closest to the position required for everyday activity.
gangrene	the death of tissue caused by interruption of the blood supply. It can result from trauma, infection, and other medical conditions.
glenoid	the socket of the shoulder.
Hodgen's straight splint	a splint that could apply traction on the leg, used especially for femur fractures. Named after John Hodgen.
humerus	the arm bone.
iatrogenic	an unexpected adverse condition caused by a physician's treatment.
ilium	the widest portion of the pelvis, palpable along one's beltline and flanks.
insertion	referring to where the tendon of a muscle attaches to a bone.
intravenous	medication or fluid injected directly into a vein
lateral	anatomical location near the side or edge.
latissimus dorsi	large muscle that spans from the back to the shoulder, where it helps to rotate the arm toward the body.
ligature	a suture that ties a vessel to prevent further bleeding.

Lisfranc amputation	an amputation through the mid-foot; named after Jacques Lisfranc, 1790-1847.
Lister-Baron, Joseph	credited with the invention of antiseptic surgery; 1827-1912.
longitudinal	in line with the extremity.
malaria	a parasitic infection carried by mosquitoes.
malunion	the healing of a bone in a deformed position.
Mathysen-Antonius	credited with development of the Plaster of Paris bandage; 1805-78. Nicolai Pirogoff is credited with simultaneous development.
medial	located near the midline.
metacarpal	a bone making up a portion of the palm.
metatarsal	a bone making up a portion of the arch of the foot.
miasmatic	a belief that foul odors cause infections.
minié ball	the .58 calibre bullet predominantly used in the Civil War.
necrosis	death of tissue.
neutral position	referring to positioning a joint in the middle of its range of motion.
open fracture	a fracture that communicates with the air. This implies a higher infection rate.
open reduction-internal fixation	a procedure where a fracture is realigned under direct vision and then fixed with a device, i.e., wires, screws, plates, that holds the fracture in place.
osteomyelitis	an infection of the bone.
palmar	toward the palm of the hand.
passive motion	moving a joint by external means. This implies that the muscles that normally move the joint are at rest.
patella	the kneecap.
phalanx	any one of the bones making up fingers or toes.
Pirogoff's amputation	an amputation through the ankle joint that preserves a portion of the heel bone (calcaneus).
posterior	in back of or toward the back.
proximal	toward the head, or center of the body.
puerperal sepsis	an infection in the genital region following childbirth or an abortion.
purulent	containing pus.
pyemia	a bacterial infection of the blood; blood poisoning.
radius	the forearm bone extending from the outer aspect of the elbow to just short of the base of the thumb.
radial	toward the radius.
resection	to remove a portion of bone or a joint.

resection arthroplasty	to remove the joint surfaces and hopefully still retain useful motion at the joint from the eventual formation of scar tissue.
sacrum	a triangular bone located at the base of the spine connecting the spine to the pelvis.
scapula	the shoulder blade.
scorbutus	scurvy; vitamin C deficiency.
sequestered	a piece of dead bone that is still located in the body.
Smith's anterior splint	a type of splint for leg fractures that can be attached to the ceiling for traction purposes; named after Nathan R. Smith.
spinous process	a normal projection of bone from the posterior aspect of the vertebra
suppurating	a wound producing pus
Syme amputation	an amputation performed through the ankle joint; named after James Syme, 1799-1870.
talus	the bone that makes up the main motion segment of the ankle.
tarsal	referring to the mid-foot bones.
tenotomy	to surgically divide a tendon.
teres major	a muscle that attaches from the scapula to the humerus and causes rotation of the arm toward the body. See also: *latissimus dorsi.*
tetanus	an infection caused by a toxin produced by the bacteria Clostridium tetani. The infection causes severe, persistent spasm of the muscles. Also known as "lock jaw."
Thomas splint	a splint applied for femur and hip fractures used successfully in World War I and still in use today. Can be used to help transport the wounded. Named after Hugh O. Thomas, 1834-91.
tibia	the main bone of the leg; the shinbone.
traction	the application of a force, usually on an extremity, to help reduce deformity.
transverse	refers to an incision made across an extremity. See also: *longitudinal.*
transverse process	bony projections that point laterally from the vertebra.
trephination	the process of cutting an opening into a bone.
trochanter	bony prominences attached to the femur, located near the hip.
ulna	the forearm bone that projects from the tip of the elbow to the inside of the wrist.
vasodialator	a drug or anesthetic agent that enlarges blood vessels, increasing the potential for shock.
Velpeau	a special bandage that immobilizes the shoulder, collarbone, and upper arm; named after Alfred Velpeau, 1795-1867.

XXV.
Endnotes

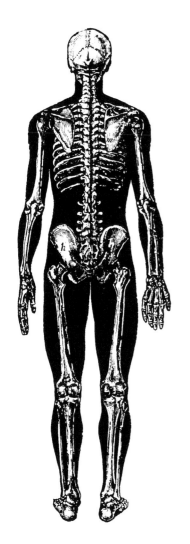

[1] Cunningham, H.H. *Doctors in Gray.* Baton Rouge, La.: Louisiana State University Press, 1958.

[2] Barnes, J.K. *Medical and Surgical History of the War of the Rebellion.* Washington, D.C.: Surgeon General's Office, 1875-1888.

[3] Ward, G.C. *The Civil War: An Illustrated History.* New York, N.Y.: Alfred A. Knopf, Inc., 1990.

[4] Adams, G.W. *Doctors in Blue.* Dayton, Oh.: Morningside House, Inc., 1985.

[5] Traill, F.A. *Michigan Veterans Facility Centennial.* Grand Rapids, Mich.: Veterans Administration, 1986.

[6] Greene, W.A. "A Case of Resection of the Shoulder-Joint," *Confederate States Medical and Surgical Journal,* 1864;1: 87-88.

[7] Bolton, J. "New Method of Treating Ununited Fracture of Long Bones," *Confederate States Medical and Surgical Journal,* 1864;1:55-6.

[8] Breeden, J.O. "Confederate General Hospitals," *North Carolina Medical Journal,* 1992; 53:110-19.

[9] Aldrete, A.J., G.M. Marron, and A.J. Wright. "The First Administration of Anesthesia in Military Surgery: On Occasion of the Mexican-American War." *Anesthesiology,* 1984; 61:585-8.

[10] Blaisdell, F.W. "Medical Advances During the Civil War," *Archives of Surgery,* 1988; 123:1045-1050.

[11] Howard, E.L. "The Effects of Minié Balls on Bone," *Confederate States Medical and Surgical Journal,* 1864; 1: 88-9.

[12] Surgeon General's Office of the Confederate States of America. *A Manual of Military Surgery.* Richmond, Va.: Ayres and Wade, 1863

[13] Swinburne, J. "Amputations: When to be Performed, and When Not Required in Military Surgery," *American Medical Times,* 1863;6:149-52.

[14] United States Sanitary Commission. "Report of a Committee of the Associate Medical Members of the United States Sanitary Commission on the Subject of the Amputations." Washington, D.C.: United States Sanitary Commission, 1863.

[15] Tripler, C.S., and G.C. Blackman. *Handbook for the Military Surgeon.* Cincinnati, Oh.: Robert Clarke and Co., 1861.

[16] United States Sanitary Commission. "Report of a Committee of the Associate Medical Members of the Sanitary Commission on the Subject of Excision of Joints for Traumatic Cause." Cambridge, Mass.: Welch, Bigelow, and Co, 1862.

[17] Hamilton, F.H. *A Practical Treatise on Fractures and Dislocations*. Philadelphia, Penn.: Henry C. Lea, 1866.

[18] Jewett, C.C. "After-Treatment of Amputations and Resections in the Third Corps Field Hospital After Gettysburg," *Boston Medical and Surgical Journal*, 1864;70:211-216.

[19] Michael, M. "Healing of Gun-Shot Wounds by First Intention," *Confederate States Medical and Surgical Journal*, 1864;1: 99-102.

[20] Surgeon General's Office. *Circular No. 2: A Report on Excisions of the Head of the Femur for Gunshot Injury*. Washington, D.C.: Government Printing Office, 1869.

[21] Evans, R.P., C.L. Nelson, and T.A. Lange. C.M. Evarts, ed. *Pathophysiology of Osteomyelitis in Surgery of the Musculoskeletal System*. New York, N.Y.: Churchill Livingstone, Inc., 1990.

[22] Le Vay, D. *The History of Orthopaedics*. Park Ridge, N.J.: Parthenon Publishing, 1990.

[23] Colon, G.A. "Innovative Civil War Surgeon," *Southern Medical Journal*, 1992; 84:411-5.

[24] Hammond, W.A., ed. *Military Medical and Surgical Essays, Prepared for the United States Sanitary Commission*. Philadelphia, Penn.: J.B. Lippincott, 1864.

[25] Hamilton, F.H. *A Practical Treatise on Fractures and Dislocations*. Philadelphia, Penn.: Henry C. Leas Son & Co., 1884.

[26] Read, J.B. "Report on Wounds of Large Joints, Made to the Confederate States Association of Navy and Army Surgeons," *Southern Medical and Surgical Journal*, 1866;21:200.

[27] Howard, B. "The Application of Sutures to Bone in Recent Gunshot Fractures, with Cases," *Medico-Chirurgical Transactions*, 1865;30:245-253.

[28] Gross, S.W. "Interesting Cases of Gunshot Wounds," *American Medical Times*,1864;8:136-138.

[29] Sorrel, F. "Gunshot Wounds—Army of Northern Virginia" [an extract from a Report on the Sickness and Mortality of the Armies of the Confederate States for 1863], *Confederate States Medical and Surgical Journal*, 1864;1:154.

[30] Eve, P.F. "The Position of the Hand in Fracture of the Fore-arm," *Confederate States Medical and Surgical Journal*, 1864;1: 212-3.

[31] Hamilton, F.H. *A Treatise on Military Surgery and Hygiene*. New York, N.Y.: Bailliere Brothers, 1865.

[32] Foote, S. *The Civil War, A Narrative*. New York, N.Y.: Random House, 1958.

[33] "United Sates Sanitary Commission: Report of a Committee of the Associate Medical Members of the Sanitary Commission on the Subject of the Treatment of Fractures in Military Surgery." Philadelphia, Penn: J.B. Lippincott, 1862.

[34] Little, J.L. *On the Use of Plaster of Paris Splints in Military Surgery*. New York, N.Y.: The United States Sanitary Commission, 1864.

[35] Murdock, R. "On Application of Smith's Anterior Splint," *Confederate States Medical and Surgical Journal*, 1864;1: 71-3.

[36] Surgeon General's Office. *Circular No.7: A Report on Amputations at the Hip-Joint in Miltary Surgery*. Washington, D.C.: Government Printing Office, 1867.

[37] Chisolm, J.J. *A Manual of Military Surgery, for Use of Surgeons in the Confederate States Army*. Richmond, Va.: West and Johnson, 1862.

[38] Author unknown. "Conservative Surgery in Compound Fracture of Femur," *Confederate States Medical and Surgical Journal*, 1864;1: 89-90.

[39] Detmold, W. "Lectures on Military Surgery," *American Medical Times*, 1863;6:73-4.

[40] Mitchell, S.W., G.R. Morehouse, and W.W. Keen. *Gunshot Wounds and Other Injuries of Nerves*. Philadelphia, Penn.: J.B. Lippincott, 1864.

[41] Author unknown. "Association to Purchase Artificial Limbs for Maimed Soldiers," *Confederate States Medical and Surgical Journal*, 1864;1:44.

[42] Author unknown. "Artificial Limbs and How to Make Them," *Confederate States Medical and Surgical Journal*, 1864;1: 59.

[43] Bly. D. "The Points of Election and Kind of Operation for Amputation of the Lower Extremities, with Reference to the Use of Artificial Limbs," *Transactions of the Medical Society of the State of New York*, 1862.

[44] Livermore, T.L. *Numbers and Losses in the Civil War in America:1861-65*. Bloomington, Ind.: Indiana University Press, 1957.

[45] Aldea, P.A., G.S. Aldea, and W.W. Shaw. "A Historical Perspective on the Changing Methods of Management for Major Trauma of the Lower Extremity" Surgery, Gynecology and Obstetrics, 1987;165:549-561.

[46] Author unknown. "Amputation, Disarticulation, and Resection Statistics of the Confederate States Army," *Confederate States Medical and Surgical Journal*, 1864;1: 77-8.

[47] Otis, G.A. *Photographs of Surgical Cases and Specimens: Taken at the Army Medical Museum*, 8 vols. Washington, D.C.: Surgeon Generals Office, 1865-72.

XXVI

Bibliography

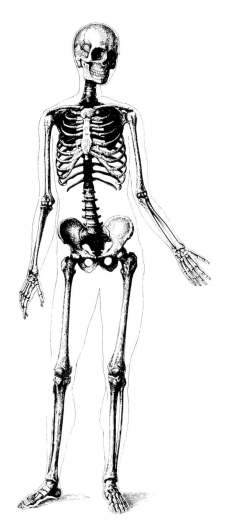

Adams, G.W. *Doctors in Blue.* Dayton, Oh.: Morningside House, Inc., 1985.

Aldea, P.A., G.S. Aldea, and W.W. Shaw. "A Historical Perspective on the Changing Methods of Management for Major Trauma of the Lower Extremity" Surgery, Gynecology and Obstetrics, 1987;165:549-561.

Aldrete, A.J., G.M. Marron, and A.J. Wright. "The First Administration of Anesthesia in Military Surgery: On Occasion of the Mexican-American War." *Anesthesiology,* 1984; 61:585-8.

"Amputation, Disarticulation, and Resection Statistics of the Confederate States Army," *Confederate States Medical and Surgical Journal,* 1864;1: 77-8. Author unknown.

"Artificial Limbs and How to Make Them," *Confederate States Medical and Surgical Journal,* 1864;1: 59. Author unknown.

"Association to Purchase Artificial Limbs for Maimed Soldiers," *Confederate States Medical and Surgical Journal,* 1864;1:44. Author unknown.

Barnes, J.K. *Medical and Surgical History of the War of the Rebellion.* Washington, D.C.: Surgeon General's Office, 1875-1888.

Blaisdell, F.W. "Medical Advances During the Civil War," *Archives of Surgery,* 1988; 123:1045-1050.

Bly, D. "The Points of Election and Kind of Operation for Amputation of the Lower Extremities, with Reference to the Use of Artificial Limbs," *Transactions of the Medical Society of New York,* 1862.

Bolton, J. "New Method of Treating Ununited Fracture of Long Bones," *Confederate States Medical and Surgical Journal,* 1864;1:55-6.

Breeden, J.O. "Confederate General Hospitals," *North Carolina Medical Journal,* 1992; 53:110-19.

Chisolm, J.J. *A Manual of Military Surgery, for Use of Surgeons in the Confederate States Army.* Richmond, Va.: West and Johnson, 1862.

Colon, G.A. "Innovative Civil War Surgeon," *Southern Medical Journal,* 1992; 84:411-5.

Conservative Surgery in Compound Fracture of Femur," *Confederate States Medical and Surgical Journal,* 1864;1: 89-90. Author unknown.

Cunningham, H.H. *Doctors in Gray.* Baton Rouge, La.: Louisiana State University Press, 1958.

Detmold, W. "Lectures on Military Surgery," *American Medical Times,* 1863;6:73-4.

Evans, R.P., C.L. Nelson, and T.A. Lange. C.M. Evarts, ed. *Pathophysiology of Osetomyelitis in Surgery of the Musculoskeletal System.* New York, N.Y.: Churchill Livingstone, 1990.

Eve, P.F. "The Position of the Hand in Fracture of the Fore-arm," *Confederate States Medical and Surgical Journal,* 1864;1: 212-3.

Foote, S. *The Civil War, A Narrative.* New York, N.Y.: Random House, 1958.

Greene, W.A. "A Case of Resection of the Shoulder-Joint," *Confederate States Medical and Surgical Journal,* 1864;1: 87-88.

Gross, S.W. "Interesting Cases of Gunshot Wounds," *American Medical Times,*1864;8:136-138.

Hamilton, F.H. *A Practical Treatise on Fractures and Dislocations.* Philadelphia, Penn.: Henry C. Lea, 1866.

Hamilton, F.H. *A Practical Treatise on Fractures and Dislocations.* Philadelphia, Penn.: Henry C. Lea's Son & Co., 1884.

Hamilton, F.H. *A Treatise on Military Surgery and Hygiene.* New York, N.Y.: Bailliere Brothers, 1865.

Hammond, W.A., ed. *Military Medical and Surgical Essays, Prepared for the United States Sanitary Commission.* Philadelphia, Penn.: J.B. Lippincott, 1864.

Howard, B. "The Application of Sutures to Bone in Recent Gunshot Fractures, with Cases," *Medico-Chirurgical Transactions,* 1865;30:245-253.

Howard, E.L. "The Effects of Minié Balls on Bone," *Confederate States Medical and Surgical Journal,* 1864; 1: 88-9.

Jewett, C.C. "After-Treatment of Amputations and Resections in the Third Corps Field Hospital After Gettysburg," *Boston Medical and Surgical Journal,* 1864;70:211-216.

Le Vay, D. *The History of Orthopaedics.* Park Ridge, N.J.: Parthenon Publishing, 1990.

Little, J.L. *On the Use of Plaster of Paris Splints in Military Surgery.* New York, N.Y.: The United States Sanitary Commission, 1864.

Livermore, T.L. *Numbers and Losses in the Civil War in America:1861-65.* Bloomington, Ind.: Indiana University Press, 1957.

Michael, M. "Healing of Gun-Shot Wounds by First Intention," *Confederate States Medical and Surgical Journal,* 1864;1: 99-102.

Mitchell, S.W., G.R. Morehouse, and W.W. Keen. *Gunshot Wounds and Other Injuries of Nerves.* Philadelphia, Penn.: J.B. Lippincott, 1864.

Murdock, R. "On Application of Smith's Anterior Splint," *Confederate States Medical and Surgical Journal,* 1864;1: 71-3.

Otis, G.A. *Photographs of Surgical Cases and Specimens: Taken at the Army Medical Museum,* 8 vols. Washington, D.C.: Surgeon Generals Office, 1865-72.

Read, J.B. "Report on Wounds of Large Joints, Made to the Confederate States Association of Navy and Army Surgeons," *Southern Medical and Surgical Journal,* 1866;21:200.

Sorrel, F. "Gunshot Wounds—Army of Northern Virginia" [an extract from a Report on the Sickness and Mortality of the Armies of the Confederate States for 1863], *Confederate States Medical and Surgical Journal,* 1864;1:154.

Surgeon General's Office. *Circular No. 2: A Report on Excisions of the Head of the Femur for Gunshot Injury.* Washington, D.C.: Government Printing Office, 1869.

Surgeon General's Office. *Circular No.7: A Report on Amputations at the Hip-Joint in Miltary Surgery.* Washington, D.C.: Government Printing Office, 1867.

Surgeon General's Office of the Confederate States of America. *A Manual of Military Surgery.* Richmond, Va.: Ayres and Wade, 1863

Swinburne, J. "Amputations: When to be Performed, and When Not Required in Military Surgery," *American Medical Times,* 1863;6:149-52.

Traill, F.A. *Michigan Veterans Facility Centennial.* Grand Rapids, Mich.: Veterans Administration, 1986.

Tripler, C.S., and G.C. Blackman. *Handbook for the Military Surgeon.* Cincinnati, Oh.: Robert Clarke and Co., 1861.

United States Sanitary Commission. "Report of a Committee of the Associate Medical Members of the United States Sanitary Commission on the Subject of the Amputations." Washington, D.C.: United States Sanitary Commision, 1863.

United States Sanitary Commission. "Report of a Committee of the Associate Medical Members of the Sanitary Commission on the Subject of Excision of Joints for Traumatic Cause." Cambridge, Mass.: Welch, Bigelow, and Co, 1862.

United States Sanitary Commission. "Report of a Committee of the Associate Medical Members of the Sanitary Commission on the Subject of the Treatment of Fractures in Military Surgery." Philadelphia, Penn: J.B. Lippincott, 1862.

Ward, G.C. *The Civil War: An Illustrated History.* New York, N.Y.: Alfred A. Knopf, Inc., 1990.

A

B

C

XXVII.
Index of Text

D

E

F

G

H

I

J

K

L

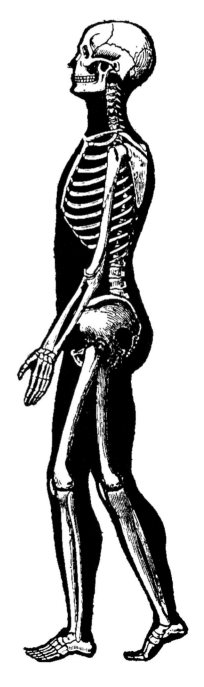

XXVIII.

Index of Cases

XXIX.

Index of Tables

About the Authors

**Co-authors
Bengtson and Kuz**

surgery at the University of Minnesota for the 1996-97 acedemic year. He currently resides in Grand Rapids with his wife, Cheryl Kuz, a practicing pediatrician.

Brad Bengtson has had a long-term interest in medical history. Since medical school, his interest has crystallized to focus on historical research on and study of Civil War medicine and surgery. He has given many regional and national talks on this subject.

A graduate of Anderson University, he received his Doctor of Medicine degree from Indiana University School of Medicine and completed his General Surgery/Plastic Surgery residency in the Michigan State University Butterworth Hospital/Grand Rapids Area Medical Education Center training programs. After finishing his residency, he completed a fellowship in cancer reconstruction at M.D. Anderson Cancer Center in Houston, Texas. Now a board certified plastic surgeon in Grand Rapids, Michigan, he specializes in the fields of microvascular surgery, cancer reconstruction, and extremity reconstruction following trauma.

Julian Kuz is a native of Minnesota now residing in Michigan. While earning his Doctor of Medicine degree at the University of Minnesota, he developed an interest in Civil War medicine upon discovering a copy of the *Medical and Surgical History of the War of the Rebellion* in the school's historical collection. This interest has culminated in a collaboration with Brad Bengtson, M.D., resulting in this, their first work: *Orthopaedic Injuries of the Civil War.*

He is currently the Chief Orthopaedic Resident at Blodgett Memorial Medical Center in Grand Rapids, Michigan, where he will be completing his training in June 1996 from the Grand Rapids Orthopaedic Surgery Residency Program. Dr. Kuz is planning a year of subspecialty training in hand and micro-

To pursue their publishing goals in this field of study, Dr. Kuz and Dr. Bengtson have formed their own publishing company—Medical Staff Press—and the newly forged team is excited about providing more written and photographic material on the all-too-often overlooked medical and surgical aspects of the war.